MW00606099

HOLD ONTO
THE LIGHT

A 365-Day Scripture Journal for Men and Women of Faith

Mark Corbin

Copyright © 2021 Mark Corbin.

All rights reserved. No part of this publication may be reproduced, distributed, or transmitted in any form or by any means, including photocopying, recording, or other electronic or mechanical methods, without the prior written permission of the publisher, except in the case of brief quotations embodied in critical reviews and certain other noncommercial uses permitted by copyright law.

ISBN: 978-1-953181-09-1 (Paperback)

Printed in the United States of America.

First printing edition 2021.

Happie Face Publishing House

God will meet you where you are. When you begin to walk with Him, use the *Hold onto the Light 365-Day Scripture Journal* to chronicle your journey. I intentionally did not date the pages as I want you to begin with God no matter the day or the season of your life you begin.

There will be days and periods when life may move your feet off the righteous path. So, when He calls to you and leads you back to Him, take the time to write about where you are, where you have been, and where you think you are being led. I believe God speaks to us all and not always in an audible voice but in our hearing, spirits, and hearts.

Enjoy using the journal to chronicle your walk with God. I pray you use these pages to write what you feel and learn and share with God and those you love.

May God keep you and may you lean upon Him to lead you through the days and nights of your life.

--- Mark Corbin

Prayer Focus: Exodus 12:2   Date: _____

This month shall be your beginning of months; it shall be the first month of the year to you.

How does this verse speak to your soul, heart, and mind?

_____

_____

_____

Daily Gratitude Prayer *(Consider a prayer like the following each morning before you start your day: Lord, thank you for this day. Lord, I am grateful for my health. Lord, thank you for trusting me to serve your people.)*

_____

_____

_____

Spend Time with God *(How did you spend time with God today? Did you pray, read scripture, or share His word with someone?)*

Daily Activity	Time	Daily Activity	Time
	6:00am		1:00pm
	7:00am		2:00pm
	8:00am		3:00pm
	9:00am		4:00pm
	10:00am		5:00pm
	11:00am		6:00pm
	12:00pm		7:00pm

Daily Prayer List *(Before you go to sleep tonight, who in your life requires prayer or what circumstance requires prayer today?)*

1. _____   2. _____

3. _____   4. _____

Prayer Focus: 1 John 3:1   Date: _____

See what great love the Father has lavished on us, that we should be called children of God! And that is what we are! The reason the world does not know us is that it did not know him.

How does this verse speak to your soul, heart, and mind?

_____

_____

_____

Daily Gratitude Prayer *(Consider a prayer like the following each morning before you start your day: Lord, thank you for this day. Lord, I am grateful for my health. Lord, thank you for trusting me to serve your people.)*

_____

_____

_____

Spend Time with God *(How did you spend time with God today? Did you pray, read scripture, or share His word with someone?)*

Daily Activity	Time	Daily Activity	Time
	6:00am		1:00pm
	7:00am		2:00pm
	8:00am		3:00pm
	9:00am		4:00pm
	10:00am		5:00pm
	11:00am		6:00pm
	12:00pm		7:00pm

Daily Prayer List *(Before you go to sleep tonight, who in your life requires prayer or what circumstance requires prayer today?)*

1. _____   2. _____

3. _____   4. _____

Prayer Focus: Exodus 35:10   Date: _____

All who are skilled among you are to come and make everything the LORD has commanded:

How does this verse speak to your soul, heart, and mind?

_____

_____

_____

Daily Gratitude Prayer *(Consider a prayer like the following each morning before you start your day: Lord, thank you for this day. Lord, I am grateful for my health. Lord, thank you for trusting me to serve your people.)*

_____

_____

_____

Spend Time with God *(How did you spend time with God today? Did you pray, read scripture, or share His word with someone?)*

Daily Activity	Time	Daily Activity	Time
	6:00am		1:00pm
	7:00am		2:00pm
	8:00am		3:00pm
	9:00am		4:00pm
	10:00am		5:00pm
	11:00am		6:00pm
	12:00pm		7:00pm

Daily Prayer List *(Before you go to sleep tonight, who in your life requires prayer or what circumstance requires prayer today?)*

1. _____   2. _____

3. _____   4. _____

Prayer Focus: Psalm 33:11   Date: _____

But the plans of the LORD stand firm forever, the purposes of his heart, through all generations.

How does this verse speak to your soul, heart, and mind?

_____

_____

_____

Daily Gratitude Prayer *(Consider a prayer like the following each morning before you start your day: Lord, thank you for this day. Lord, I am grateful for my health. Lord, thank you for trusting me to serve your people.)*

_____

_____

_____

Spend Time with God *(How did you spend time with God today? Did you pray, read scripture, or share His word with someone?)*

Daily Activity	Time	Daily Activity	Time
	6:00am		1:00pm
	7:00am		2:00pm
	8:00am		3:00pm
	9:00am		4:00pm
	10:00am		5:00pm
	11:00am		6:00pm
	12:00pm		7:00pm

Daily Prayer List *(Before you go to sleep tonight, who in your life requires prayer or what circumstance requires prayer today?)*

1. _____ 2. _____

3. _____ 4. _____

Prayer Focus: Psalm 93:4   Date: _____

Mightier than the thunder of the great waters, mightier than the breakers of the sea— the LORD on high is mighty.

How does this verse speak to your soul, heart, and mind?

_____

_____

_____

Daily Gratitude Prayer *(Consider a prayer like the following each morning before you start your day: Lord, thank you for this day. Lord, I am grateful for my health. Lord, thank you for trusting me to serve your people.)*

_____

_____

_____

Spend Time with God *(How did you spend time with God today? Did you pray, read scripture, or share His word with someone?)*

Daily Activity	Time	Daily Activity	Time
	6:00am		1:00pm
	7:00am		2:00pm
	8:00am		3:00pm
	9:00am		4:00pm
	10:00am		5:00pm
	11:00am		6:00pm
	12:00pm		7:00pm

Daily Prayer List *(Before you go to sleep tonight, who in your life requires prayer or what circumstance requires prayer today?)*

1. _____   2. _____

3. _____   4. _____

Prayer Focus: Psalm 34:15

Date: _____

The eyes of the LORD are on the righteous, and his ears are attentive to their cry.

How does this verse speak to your soul, heart, and mind?

_____

_____

_____

Daily Gratitude Prayer *(Consider a prayer like the following each morning before you start your day: Lord, thank you for this day. Lord, I am grateful for my health. Lord, thank you for trusting me to serve your people.)*

_____

_____

_____

Spend Time with God *(How did you spend time with God today? Did you pray, read scripture, or share His word with someone?)*

Daily Activity	Time	Daily Activity	Time
	6:00am		1:00pm
	7:00am		2:00pm
	8:00am		3:00pm
	9:00am		4:00pm
	10:00am		5:00pm
	11:00am		6:00pm
	12:00pm		7:00pm

Daily Prayer List (Before you go to sleep tonight, who in your life requires prayer or what circumstance requires prayer today?)

1. _____

2. _____

3. _____

4. _____

Prayer Focus: Job 42:2   Date: _____

I know that you can do all things; no purpose of yours can be thwarted.

How does this verse speak to your soul, heart, and mind?

_____

_____

_____

Daily Gratitude Prayer *(Consider a prayer like the following each morning before you start your day: Lord, thank you for this day. Lord, I am grateful for my health. Lord, thank you for trusting me to serve your people.)*

_____

_____

_____

Spend Time with God *(How did you spend time with God today? Did you pray, read scripture, or share His word with someone?)*

Daily Activity	Time	Daily Activity	Time
	6:00am		1:00pm
	7:00am		2:00pm
	8:00am		3:00pm
	9:00am		4:00pm
	10:00am		5:00pm
	11:00am		6:00pm
	12:00pm		7:00pm

Daily Prayer List *(Before you go to sleep tonight, who in your life requires prayer or what circumstance requires prayer today?)*

1. _____   2. _____

3. _____   4. _____

Prayer Focus: Ephesians 3:16   Date: _____

I pray that out of his glorious riches he may strengthen you with power through his Spirit in your inner being.

How does this verse speak to your soul, heart, and mind?

_____

_____

_____

Daily Gratitude Prayer *(Consider a prayer like the following each morning before you start your day: Lord, thank you for this day. Lord, I am grateful for my health. Lord, thank you for trusting me to serve your people.)*

_____

_____

_____

Spend Time with God *(How did you spend time with God today? Did you pray, read scripture, or share His word with someone?)*

Daily Activity	Time	Daily Activity	Time
	6:00am		1:00pm
	7:00am		2:00pm
	8:00am		3:00pm
	9:00am		4:00pm
	10:00am		5:00pm
	11:00am		6:00pm
	12:00pm		7:00pm

Daily Prayer List *(Before you go to sleep tonight, who in your life requires prayer or what circumstance requires prayer today?)*

1. _____   2. _____

3. _____   4. _____

Prayer Focus: Deuteronomy 8:6   Date: _____

Observe the commands of the LORD your God, walking in obedience to him and revering him.

How does this verse speak to your soul, heart, and mind?

_____

_____

_____

Daily Gratitude Prayer *(Consider a prayer like the following each morning before you start your day: Lord, thank you for this day. Lord, I am grateful for my health. Lord, thank you for trusting me to serve your people.)*

_____

_____

_____

Spend Time with God *(How did you spend time with God today? Did you pray, read scripture, or share His word with someone?)*

Daily Activity	Time	Daily Activity	Time
	6:00am		1:00pm
	7:00am		2:00pm
	8:00am		3:00pm
	9:00am		4:00pm
	10:00am		5:00pm
	11:00am		6:00pm
	12:00pm		7:00pm

Daily Prayer List *(Before you go to sleep tonight, who in your life requires prayer or what circumstance requires prayer today?)*

1. _____   2. _____

3. _____   4. _____

Prayer Focus: Ephesians 5:15 -16   Date: _____

Therefore, be careful how you walk, not as unwise men but as wise, making the most of your time, because the days are evil.

How does this verse speak to your soul, heart, and mind?

_____

_____

_____

Daily Gratitude Prayer *(Consider a prayer like the following each morning before you start your day: Lord, thank you for this day. Lord, I am grateful for my health. Lord, thank you for trusting me to serve your people.)*

_____

_____

_____

Spend Time with God *(How did you spend time with God today? Did you pray, read scripture, or share His word with someone?)*

Daily Activity	Time	Daily Activity	Time
	6:00am		1:00pm
	7:00am		2:00pm
	8:00am		3:00pm
	9:00am		4:00pm
	10:00am		5:00pm
	11:00am		6:00pm
	12:00pm		7:00pm

Daily Prayer List *(Before you go to sleep tonight, who in your life requires prayer or what circumstance requires prayer today?)*

1. _____

2. _____

3. _____

4. _____

Prayer Focus: John 14:1   Date: _____

Do not let your hearts be troubled. You believe in God; believe also in me.

How does this verse speak to your soul, heart, and mind?

_____

_____

_____

Daily Gratitude Prayer *(Consider a prayer like the following each morning before you start your day: Lord, thank you for this day. Lord, I am grateful for my health. Lord, thank you for trusting me to serve your people.)*

_____

_____

_____

Spend Time with God *(How did you spend time with God today? Did you pray, read scripture, or share His word with someone?)*

Daily Activity	Time	Daily Activity	Time
	6:00am		1:00pm
	7:00am		2:00pm
	8:00am		3:00pm
	9:00am		4:00pm
	10:00am		5:00pm
	11:00am		6:00pm
	12:00pm		7:00pm

Daily Prayer List *(Before you go to sleep tonight, who in your life requires prayer or what circumstance requires prayer today?)*

1. _____   2. _____

3. _____   4. _____

Prayer Focus: Psalm 34:8   Date: _____

Taste and see that the LORD is good; blessed is the one who takes refuge in him.

How does this verse speak to your soul, heart, and mind?

_____

_____

_____

Daily Gratitude Prayer *(Consider a prayer like the following each morning before you start your day: Lord, thank you for this day. Lord, I am grateful for my health. Lord, thank you for trusting me to serve your people.)*

_____

_____

_____

Spend Time with God *(How did you spend time with God today? Did you pray, read scripture, or share His word with someone?)*

Daily Activity	Time	Daily Activity	Time
	6:00am		1:00pm
	7:00am		2:00pm
	8:00am		3:00pm
	9:00am		4:00pm
	10:00am		5:00pm
	11:00am		6:00pm
	12:00pm		7:00pm

Daily Prayer List *(Before you go to sleep tonight, who in your life requires prayer or what circumstance requires prayer today?)*

1. _____   2. _____

3. _____   4. _____

Prayer Focus: Ezekiel 38:7   Date: _____

Get ready; be prepared! Keep all the armies around you mobilized and take command of them.

How does this verse speak to your soul, heart, and mind?

_____

_____

_____

Daily Gratitude Prayer *(Consider a prayer like the following each morning before you start your day: Lord, thank you for this day. Lord, I am grateful for my health. Lord, thank you for trusting me to serve your people.)*

_____

_____

_____

Spend Time with God *(How did you spend time with God today? Did you pray, read scripture, or share His word with someone?)*

Daily Activity	Time	Daily Activity	Time
	6:00am		1:00pm
	7:00am		2:00pm
	8:00am		3:00pm
	9:00am		4:00pm
	10:00am		5:00pm
	11:00am		6:00pm
	12:00pm		7:00pm

Daily Prayer List *(Before you go to sleep tonight, who in your life requires prayer or what circumstance requires prayer today?)*

1. _____   2. _____

3. _____   4. _____

Prayer Focus: Romans 8:26   Date: _____

In the same way, the Spirit helps us in our weakness. We do not know what we ought to pray for, but the Spirit himself intercedes for us through wordless groans.

How does this verse speak to your soul, heart, and mind?

_____

_____

_____

Daily Gratitude Prayer *(Consider a prayer like the following each morning before you start your day: Lord, thank you for this day. Lord, I am grateful for my health. Lord, thank you for trusting me to serve your people.)*

_____

_____

_____

Spend Time with God *(How did you spend time with God today? Did you pray, read scripture, or share His word with someone?)*

Daily Activity	Time	Daily Activity	Time
	6:00am		1:00pm
	7:00am		2:00pm
	8:00am		3:00pm
	9:00am		4:00pm
	10:00am		5:00pm
	11:00am		6:00pm
	12:00pm		7:00pm

Daily Prayer List *(Before you go to sleep tonight, who in your life requires prayer or what circumstance requires prayer today?)*

1. _____

2. _____

3. _____

4. _____

Prayer Focus: 2 Corinthians 8:11   Date: _____

But now finish doing it also, so that just as there was the willingness to desire it, so there may be also the completion of it by your ability.

How does this verse speak to your soul, heart, and mind?

_____

_____

_____

Daily Gratitude Prayer *(Consider a prayer like the following each morning before you start your day: Lord, thank you for this day. Lord, I am grateful for my health. Lord, thank you for trusting me to serve your people.)*

_____

_____

_____

Spend Time with God *(How did you spend time with God today? Did you pray, read scripture, or share His word with someone?)*

Daily Activity	Time	Daily Activity	Time
	6:00am		1:00pm
	7:00am		2:00pm
	8:00am		3:00pm
	9:00am		4:00pm
	10:00am		5:00pm
	11:00am		6:00pm
	12:00pm		7:00pm

Daily Prayer List *(Before you go to sleep tonight, who in your life requires prayer or what circumstance requires prayer today?)*

1. _____   2. _____

3. _____   4. _____

Prayer Focus: Genesis 13:17   Date: _____

Arise, walk in the land through its length and its width, for I give it to you.

How does this verse speak to your soul, heart, and mind?

_____

_____

_____

Daily Gratitude Prayer *(Consider a prayer like the following each morning before you start your day: Lord, thank you for this day. Lord, I am grateful for my health. Lord, thank you for trusting me to serve your people.)*

_____

_____

_____

Spend Time with God *(How did you spend time with God today? Did you pray, read scripture, or share His word with someone?)*

Daily Activity	Time	Daily Activity	Time
	6:00am		1:00pm
	7:00am		2:00pm
	8:00am		3:00pm
	9:00am		4:00pm
	10:00am		5:00pm
	11:00am		6:00pm
	12:00pm		7:00pm

Daily Prayer List *(Before you go to sleep tonight, who in your life requires prayer or what circumstance requires prayer today?)*

1. _____   2. _____

3. _____   4. _____

Prayer Focus: Psalm 143:10

Date: _____

Teach me to do your will, for you are my God; may your good Spirit lead me on level ground.

How does this verse speak to your soul, heart, and mind?

_____

_____

_____

Daily Gratitude Prayer *(Consider a prayer like the following each morning before you start your day: Lord, thank you for this day. Lord, I am grateful for my health. Lord, thank you for trusting me to serve your people.)*

_____

_____

_____

Spend Time with God *(How did you spend time with God today? Did you pray, read scripture, or share His word with someone?)*

Daily Activity	Time	Daily Activity	Time
	6:00am		1:00pm
	7:00am		2:00pm
	8:00am		3:00pm
	9:00am		4:00pm
	10:00am		5:00pm
	11:00am		6:00pm
	12:00pm		7:00pm

Daily Prayer List *(Before you go to sleep tonight, who in your life requires prayer or what circumstance requires prayer today?)*

1. _____   2. _____

3. _____   4. _____

Prayer Focus: Proverbs 18:20   Date: _____

From the fruit of their mouth a person's stomach is filled; with the harvest of their lips, they are satisfied.

How does this verse speak to your soul, heart, and mind?

_____

_____

_____

Daily Gratitude Prayer *(Consider a prayer like the following each morning before you start your day: Lord, thank you for this day. Lord, I am grateful for my health. Lord, thank you for trusting me to serve your people.)*

_____

_____

_____

Spend Time with God *(How did you spend time with God today? Did you pray, read scripture, or share His word with someone?)*

Daily Activity	Time	Daily Activity	Time
	6:00am		1:00pm
	7:00am		2:00pm
	8:00am		3:00pm
	9:00am		4:00pm
	10:00am		5:00pm
	11:00am		6:00pm
	12:00pm		7:00pm

Daily Prayer List *(Before you go to sleep tonight, who in your life requires prayer or what circumstance requires prayer today?)*

1. _____   2. _____

3. _____   4. _____

Prayer Focus: 2 Timothy 1:6   Date: _____

For this reason, I remind you to fan into flame the gift of God, which is in you through the laying on of my hands.

How does this verse speak to your soul, heart, and mind?

_____

_____

_____

Daily Gratitude Prayer *(Consider a prayer like the following each morning before you start your day: Lord, thank you for this day. Lord, I am grateful for my health. Lord, thank you for trusting me to serve your people.)*

_____

_____

_____

Spend Time with God *(How did you spend time with God today? Did you pray, read scripture, or share His word with someone?)*

Daily Activity	Time	Daily Activity	Time
	6:00am		1:00pm
	7:00am		2:00pm
	8:00am		3:00pm
	9:00am		4:00pm
	10:00am		5:00pm
	11:00am		6:00pm
	12:00pm		7:00pm

Daily Prayer List *(Before you go to sleep tonight, who in your life requires prayer or what circumstance requires prayer today?)*

1. _____   2. _____

3. _____   4. _____

Prayer Focus: 1 Corinthians 3:11   Date: _____

For no one can lay any foundation other than the one already laid, which is Jesus Christ.

How does this verse speak to your soul, heart, and mind?

_____

_____

_____

Daily Gratitude Prayer *(Consider a prayer like the following each morning before you start your day: Lord, thank you for this day. Lord, I am grateful for my health. Lord, thank you for trusting me to serve your people.)*

_____

_____

_____

Spend Time with God *(How did you spend time with God today? Did you pray, read scripture, or share His word with someone?)*

Daily Activity	Time	Daily Activity	Time
	6:00am		1:00pm
	7:00am		2:00pm
	8:00am		3:00pm
	9:00am		4:00pm
	10:00am		5:00pm
	11:00am		6:00pm
	12:00pm		7:00pm

Daily Prayer List *(Before you go to sleep tonight, who in your life requires prayer or what circumstance requires prayer today?)*

1. _____   2. _____

3. _____   4. _____

Prayer Focus: Proverbs 22:29   Date: _____

Do you see someone skilled in their work? They will serve before kings; they will not serve before officials of low rank.

How does this verse speak to your soul, heart, and mind?

_____

_____

_____

Daily Gratitude Prayer *(Consider a prayer like the following each morning before you start your day: Lord, thank you for this day. Lord, I am grateful for my health. Lord, thank you for trusting me to serve your people.)*

_____

_____

_____

Spend Time with God *(How did you spend time with God today? Did you pray, read scripture, or share His word with someone?)*

Daily Activity	Time	Daily Activity	Time
	6:00am		1:00pm
	7:00am		2:00pm
	8:00am		3:00pm
	9:00am		4:00pm
	10:00am		5:00pm
	11:00am		6:00pm
	12:00pm		7:00pm

Daily Prayer List *(Before you go to sleep tonight, who in your life requires prayer or what circumstance requires prayer today?)*

1. _____   2. _____

3. _____   4. _____

Prayer Focus: Ecclesiastes 3:1   Date: _____

There is a time for everything, and a season for every activity under the heavens.

How does this verse speak to your soul, heart, and mind?

_____

_____

_____

Daily Gratitude Prayer *(Consider a prayer like the following each morning before you start your day: Lord, thank you for this day. Lord, I am grateful for my health. Lord, thank you for trusting me to serve your people.)*

_____

_____

_____

Spend Time with God *(How did you spend time with God today? Did you pray, read scripture, or share His word with someone?)*

Daily Activity	Time	Daily Activity	Time
	6:00am		1:00pm
	7:00am		2:00pm
	8:00am		3:00pm
	9:00am		4:00pm
	10:00am		5:00pm
	11:00am		6:00pm
	12:00pm		7:00pm

Daily Prayer List *(Before you go to sleep tonight, who in your life requires prayer or what circumstance requires prayer today?)*

1. _____   2. _____

3. _____   4. _____

Prayer Focus: Habakkuk 1:5   Date: _____

Look among the nations and watch— Be utterly astounded! For I will work a work in your days Which you would not believe, though it were told you.

How does this verse speak to your soul, heart, and mind?

_____

_____

_____

Daily Gratitude Prayer *(Consider a prayer like the following each morning before you start your day: Lord, thank you for this day. Lord, I am grateful for my health. Lord, thank you for trusting me to serve your people.)*

_____

_____

_____

Spend Time with God *(How did you spend time with God today? Did you pray, read scripture, or share His word with someone?)*

Daily Activity	Time	Daily Activity	Time
	6:00am		1:00pm
	7:00am		2:00pm
	8:00am		3:00pm
	9:00am		4:00pm
	10:00am		5:00pm
	11:00am		6:00pm
	12:00pm		7:00pm

Daily Prayer List *(Before you go to sleep tonight, who in your life requires prayer or what circumstance requires prayer today?)*

1. _____   2. _____

3. _____   4. _____

Prayer Focus: 2 Corinthians 4:15   Date: _____

All this is for your benefit, so that the grace that is reaching more and more people may cause thanksgiving to overflow to the glory of God.

How does this verse speak to your soul, heart, and mind?

_____

_____

_____

Daily Gratitude Prayer *(Consider a prayer like the following each morning before you start your day: Lord, thank you for this day. Lord, I am grateful for my health. Lord, thank you for trusting me to serve your people.)*

_____

_____

_____

Spend Time with God *(How did you spend time with God today? Did you pray, read scripture, or share His word with someone?)*

Daily Activity	Time	Daily Activity	Time
	6:00am		1:00pm
	7:00am		2:00pm
	8:00am		3:00pm
	9:00am		4:00pm
	10:00am		5:00pm
	11:00am		6:00pm
	12:00pm		7:00pm

Daily Prayer List *(Before you go to sleep tonight, who in your life requires prayer or what circumstance requires prayer today?)*

1. _____   2. _____

3. _____   4. _____

Prayer Focus: Deuteronomy 10:11   Date: _____

Go, "the LORD said to me, "and lead the people on their way, so that they may enter and possess the land I swore to their ancestors to give them.

How does this verse speak to your soul, heart, and mind?

_____

_____

_____

Daily Gratitude Prayer *(Consider a prayer like the following each morning before you start your day: Lord, thank you for this day. Lord, I am grateful for my health. Lord, thank you for trusting me to serve your people.)*

_____

_____

_____

Spend Time with God *(How did you spend time with God today? Did you pray, read scripture, or share His word with someone?)*

Daily Activity	Time	Daily Activity	Time
	6:00am		1:00pm
	7:00am		2:00pm
	8:00am		3:00pm
	9:00am		4:00pm
	10:00am		5:00pm
	11:00am		6:00pm
	12:00pm		7:00pm

Daily Prayer List *(Before you go to sleep tonight, who in your life requires prayer or what circumstance requires prayer today?)*

1. _____   2. _____

3. _____   4. _____

Prayer Focus: Hebrews 12:28   Date: _____

Therefore, since we are receiving a kingdom that cannot be shaken, let us be thankful, and so worship God acceptably with reverence and awe.

How does this verse speak to your soul, heart, and mind?

_____

_____

_____

Daily Gratitude Prayer *(Consider a prayer like the following each morning before you start your day: Lord, thank you for this day. Lord, I am grateful for my health. Lord, thank you for trusting me to serve your people.)*

_____

_____

_____

Spend Time with God *(How did you spend time with God today? Did you pray, read scripture, or share His word with someone?)*

Daily Activity	Time	Daily Activity	Time
	6:00am		1:00pm
	7:00am		2:00pm
	8:00am		3:00pm
	9:00am		4:00pm
	10:00am		5:00pm
	11:00am		6:00pm
	12:00pm		7:00pm

Daily Prayer List *(Before you go to sleep tonight, who in your life requires prayer or what circumstance requires prayer today?)*

1. _____   2. _____

3. _____   4. _____

Prayer Focus: 1 Corinthians 12:6   Date: _____

There are different kinds of working, but in all of them and in everyone it is the same God at work.

How does this verse speak to your soul, heart, and mind?

_____

_____

_____

Daily Gratitude Prayer *(Consider a prayer like the following each morning before you start your day: Lord, thank you for this day. Lord, I am grateful for my health. Lord, thank you for trusting me to serve your people.)*

_____

_____

_____

Spend Time with God *(How did you spend time with God today? Did you pray, read scripture, or share His word with someone?)*

Daily Activity	Time	Daily Activity	Time
	6:00am		1:00pm
	7:00am		2:00pm
	8:00am		3:00pm
	9:00am		4:00pm
	10:00am		5:00pm
	11:00am		6:00pm
	12:00pm		7:00pm

Daily Prayer List *(Before you go to sleep tonight, who in your life requires prayer or what circumstance requires prayer today?)*

1. _____   2. _____

3. _____   4. _____

Prayer Focus: Romans 5: 3-4   Date: _____

And not only this, but we also exult in our tribulations, knowing that tribulation brings about perseverance; and perseverance, proven character; and proven character, hope.

How does this verse speak to your soul, heart, and mind?

_____

_____

_____

Daily Gratitude Prayer *(Consider a prayer like the following each morning before you start your day: Lord, thank you for this day. Lord, I am grateful for my health. Lord, thank you for trusting me to serve your people.)*

_____

_____

_____

Spend Time with God *(How did you spend time with God today? Did you pray, read scripture, or share His word with someone?)*

Daily Activity	Time	Daily Activity	Time
	6:00am		1:00pm
	7:00am		2:00pm
	8:00am		3:00pm
	9:00am		4:00pm
	10:00am		5:00pm
	11:00am		6:00pm
	12:00pm		7:00pm

Daily Prayer List *(Before you go to sleep tonight, who in your life requires prayer or what circumstance requires prayer today?)*

1. _____   2. _____

3. _____   4. _____

Prayer Focus: Proverbs 17:17

Date: _____

A friend loves at all times, and a brother is born for a time of adversity.

How does this verse speak to your soul, heart, and mind?

_____

_____

_____

Daily Gratitude Prayer *(Consider a prayer like the following each morning before you start your day: Lord, thank you for this day. Lord, I am grateful for my health. Lord, thank you for trusting me to serve your people.)*

_____

_____

_____

Spend Time with God *(How did you spend time with God today? Did you pray, read scripture, or share His word with someone?)*

Daily Activity	Time	Daily Activity	Time
	6:00am		1:00pm
	7:00am		2:00pm
	8:00am		3:00pm
	9:00am		4:00pm
	10:00am		5:00pm
	11:00am		6:00pm
	12:00pm		7:00pm

Daily Prayer List *(Before you go to sleep tonight, who in your life requires prayer or what circumstance requires prayer today?)*

1. _____

2. _____

3. _____

4. _____

Prayer Focus: Isaiah 30:21   Date: _____

Whether you turn to the right or to the left, your ears will hear a voice behind you, saying, "This is the way; walk in it."

How does this verse speak to your soul, heart, and mind?

_____

_____

_____

Daily Gratitude Prayer *(Consider a prayer like the following each morning before you start your day: Lord, thank you for this day. Lord, I am grateful for my health. Lord, thank you for trusting me to serve your people.)*

_____

_____

_____

Spend Time with God *(How did you spend time with God today? Did you pray, read scripture, or share His word with someone?)*

Daily Activity	Time	Daily Activity	Time
	6:00am		1:00pm
	7:00am		2:00pm
	8:00am		3:00pm
	9:00am		4:00pm
	10:00am		5:00pm
	11:00am		6:00pm
	12:00pm		7:00pm

Daily Prayer List *(Before you go to sleep tonight, who in your life requires prayer or what circumstance requires prayer today?)*

1. _____   2. _____

3. _____   4. _____

Prayer Focus: Hebrews 11:3   Date: _____

By faith we understand that the universe was formed at God's command, so that what is seen was not made out of what was visible.

How does this verse speak to your soul, heart, and mind?

_____

_____

_____

Daily Gratitude Prayer *(Consider a prayer like the following each morning before you start your day: Lord, thank you for this day. Lord, I am grateful for my health. Lord, thank you for trusting me to serve your people.)*

_____

_____

_____

Spend Time with God *(How did you spend time with God today? Did you pray, read scripture, or share His word with someone?)*

Daily Activity	Time	Daily Activity	Time
	6:00am		1:00pm
	7:00am		2:00pm
	8:00am		3:00pm
	9:00am		4:00pm
	10:00am		5:00pm
	11:00am		6:00pm
	12:00pm		7:00pm

Daily Prayer List *(Before you go to sleep tonight, who in your life requires prayer or what circumstance requires prayer today?)*

1. _____   2. _____

3. _____   4. _____

Prayer Focus: 1 Thessalonians 5:21 (ESV)   Date: _____

But test everything; hold fast what is good.

How does this verse speak to your soul, heart, and mind?

_____

_____

_____

Daily Gratitude Prayer *(Consider a prayer like the following each morning before you start your day: Lord, thank you for this day. Lord, I am grateful for my health. Lord, thank you for trusting me to serve your people.)*

_____

_____

_____

Spend Time with God *(How did you spend time with God today? Did you pray, read scripture, or share His word with someone?)*

Daily Activity	Time	Daily Activity	Time
	6:00am		1:00pm
	7:00am		2:00pm
	8:00am		3:00pm
	9:00am		4:00pm
	10:00am		5:00pm
	11:00am		6:00pm
	12:00pm		7:00pm

Daily Prayer List (Before you go to sleep tonight, who in your life requires prayer or what circumstance requires prayer today?)

1. _____   2. _____

3. _____   4. _____

Prayer Focus: 2 Corinthians 8:12   Date: _____

For if the willingness is there, the gift is acceptable according to what one has, not according to what one does not have.

How does this verse speak to your soul, heart, and mind?

_____

_____

_____

Daily Gratitude Prayer *(Consider a prayer like the following each morning before you start your day: Lord, thank you for this day. Lord, I am grateful for my health. Lord, thank you for trusting me to serve your people.)*

_____

_____

_____

Spend Time with God *(How did you spend time with God today? Did you pray, read scripture, or share His word with someone?)*

Daily Activity	Time	Daily Activity	Time
	6:00am		1:00pm
	7:00am		2:00pm
	8:00am		3:00pm
	9:00am		4:00pm
	10:00am		5:00pm
	11:00am		6:00pm
	12:00pm		7:00pm

Daily Prayer List *(Before you go to sleep tonight, who in your life requires prayer or what circumstance requires prayer today?)*

1. _____   2. _____

3. _____   4. _____

Prayer Focus: 2 Timothy 1:6   Date: _____

For this reason, I remind you to fan into flame the gift of God, which is in you through the laying on of my hands.

How does this verse speak to your soul, heart, and mind?

_____

_____

_____

Daily Gratitude Prayer *(Consider a prayer like the following each morning before you start your day: Lord, thank you for this day. Lord, I am grateful for my health. Lord, thank you for trusting me to serve your people.)*

_____

_____

_____

Spend Time with God *(How did you spend time with God today? Did you pray, read scripture, or share His word with someone?)*

Daily Activity	Time	Daily Activity	Time
	6:00am		1:00pm
	7:00am		2:00pm
	8:00am		3:00pm
	9:00am		4:00pm
	10:00am		5:00pm
	11:00am		6:00pm
	12:00pm		7:00pm

Daily Prayer List *(Before you go to sleep tonight, who in your life requires prayer or what circumstance requires prayer today?)*

1. _____   2. _____

3. _____   4. _____

Prayer Focus: Numbers 16:48   Date: _____

And he stood between the dead and the living; so, the plague was stopped.

How does this verse speak to your soul, heart, and mind?

_____

_____

_____

Daily Gratitude Prayer *(Consider a prayer like the following each morning before you start your day: Lord, thank you for this day. Lord, I am grateful for my health. Lord, thank you for trusting me to serve your people.)*

_____

_____

_____

Spend Time with God *(How did you spend time with God today? Did you pray, read scripture, or share His word with someone?)*

Daily Activity	Time	Daily Activity	Time
	6:00am		1:00pm
	7:00am		2:00pm
	8:00am		3:00pm
	9:00am		4:00pm
	10:00am		5:00pm
	11:00am		6:00pm
	12:00pm		7:00pm

Daily Prayer List *(Before you go to sleep tonight, who in your life requires prayer or what circumstance requires prayer today?)*

1. _____   2. _____

3. _____   4. _____

Prayer Focus: 2 Corinthians 4:18   Date: _____

So, we fix our eyes not on what is seen, but on what is unseen, since what is seen is temporary, but what is unseen is eternal.

How does this verse speak to your soul, heart, and mind?

_____

_____

_____

Daily Gratitude Prayer *(Consider a prayer like the following each morning before you start your day: Lord, thank you for this day. Lord, I am grateful for my health. Lord, thank you for trusting me to serve your people.)*

_____

_____

_____

Spend Time with God *(How did you spend time with God today? Did you pray, read scripture, or share His word with someone?)*

Daily Activity	Time	Daily Activity	Time
	6:00am		1:00pm
	7:00am		2:00pm
	8:00am		3:00pm
	9:00am		4:00pm
	10:00am		5:00pm
	11:00am		6:00pm
	12:00pm		7:00pm

Daily Prayer List *(Before you go to sleep tonight, who in your life requires prayer or what circumstance requires prayer today?)*

1. _____   2. _____

3. _____   4. _____

Prayer Focus: Micah 7:8   Date: _____

Do not rejoice over me, my enemy; When I fall, I will arise; When I sit in darkness, The LORD will be a light to me.

How does this verse speak to your soul, heart, and mind?

_____

_____

_____

Daily Gratitude Prayer *(Consider a prayer like the following each morning before you start your day: Lord, thank you for this day. Lord, I am grateful for my health. Lord, thank you for trusting me to serve your people.)*

_____

_____

_____

Spend Time with God *(How did you spend time with God today? Did you pray, read scripture, or share His word with someone?)*

Daily Activity	Time	Daily Activity	Time
	6:00am		1:00pm
	7:00am		2:00pm
	8:00am		3:00pm
	9:00am		4:00pm
	10:00am		5:00pm
	11:00am		6:00pm
	12:00pm		7:00pm

Daily Prayer List *(Before you go to sleep tonight, who in your life requires prayer or what circumstance requires prayer today?)*

1. _____   2. _____

3. _____   4. _____

Pyer Focus: Psalm 121:7-8   Date: _____

The LORD will keep you from all harm— he will watch over your life. the LORD will watch over your coming and going both now and forevermore.

How does this verse speak to your soul, heart, and mind?

_____

_____

_____

Daily Gratitude Prayer *(Consider a prayer like the following each morning before you start your day: Lord, thank you for this day. Lord, I am grateful for my health. Lord, thank you for trusting me to serve your people.)*

_____

_____

_____

Spend Time with God *(How did you spend time with God today? Did you pray, read scripture, or share His word with someone?)*

Daily Activity	Time	Daily Activity	Time
	6:00am		1:00pm
	7:00am		2:00pm
	8:00am		3:00pm
	9:00am		4:00pm
	10:00am		5:00pm
	11:00am		6:00pm
	12:00pm		7:00pm

Daily Prayer List *(Before you go to sleep tonight, who in your life requires prayer or what circumstance requires prayer today?)*

1. _____   2. _____

3. _____   4. _____

Prayer Focus: Deuteronomy 2:3   Date: _____

You have circled this mountain long enough. Now turn north.

How does this verse speak to your soul, heart, and mind?

_____

_____

_____

Daily Gratitude Prayer *(Consider a prayer like the following each morning before you start your day: Lord, thank you for this day. Lord, I am grateful for my health. Lord, thank you for trusting me to serve your people.)*

_____

_____

_____

Spend Time with God *(How did you spend time with God today? Did you pray, read scripture, or share His word with someone?)*

Daily Activity	Time	Daily Activity	Time
	6:00am		1:00pm
	7:00am		2:00pm
	8:00am		3:00pm
	9:00am		4:00pm
	10:00am		5:00pm
	11:00am		6:00pm
	12:00pm		7:00pm

Daily Prayer List *(Before you go to sleep tonight, who in your life requires prayer or what circumstance requires prayer today?)*

1. _____ 2. _____

3. _____ 4. _____

Prayer Focus: Jeremiah 33:3   Date: _____

Call to me and I will answer you and tell you great and unsearchable things you do not know.

How does this verse speak to your soul, heart, and mind?

_____

_____

_____

Daily Gratitude Prayer *(Consider a prayer like the following each morning before you start your day: Lord, thank you for this day. Lord, I am grateful for my health. Lord, thank you for trusting me to serve your people.)*

_____

_____

_____

Spend Time with God *(How did you spend time with God today? Did you pray, read scripture, or share His word with someone?)*

Daily Activity	Time	Daily Activity	Time
	6:00am		1:00pm
	7:00am		2:00pm
	8:00am		3:00pm
	9:00am		4:00pm
	10:00am		5:00pm
	11:00am		6:00pm
	12:00pm		7:00pm

Daily Prayer List *(Before you go to sleep tonight, who in your life requires prayer or what circumstance requires prayer today?)*

1. _____   2. _____

3. _____   4. _____

Prayer Focus: Mark 11:24   Date: _____

Therefore, I tell you, whatever you ask for in prayer, believe that you have received it, and it will be yours.

How does this verse speak to your soul, heart, and mind?

_____

_____

_____

Daily Gratitude Prayer *(Consider a prayer like the following each morning before you start your day: Lord, thank you for this day. Lord, I am grateful for my health. Lord, thank you for trusting me to serve your people.)*

_____

_____

_____

Spend Time with God *(How did you spend time with God today? Did you pray, read scripture, or share His word with someone?)*

Daily Activity	Time	Daily Activity	Time
	6:00am		1:00pm
	7:00am		2:00pm
	8:00am		3:00pm
	9:00am		4:00pm
	10:00am		5:00pm
	11:00am		6:00pm
	12:00pm		7:00pm

Daily Prayer List *(Before you go to sleep tonight, who in your life requires prayer or what circumstance requires prayer today?)*

1. _____   2. _____

3. _____   4. _____

Prayer Focus: John 8:32   Date: _____

Then you will know the truth, and the truth will set you free.

How does this verse speak to your soul, heart, and mind?

_____

_____

_____

Daily Gratitude Prayer *(Consider a prayer like the following each morning before you start your day: Lord, thank you for this day. Lord, I am grateful for my health. Lord, thank you for trusting me to serve your people.)*

_____

_____

_____

Spend Time with God *(How did you spend time with God today? Did you pray, read scripture, or share His word with someone?)*

Daily Activity	Time	Daily Activity	Time
	6:00am		1:00pm
	7:00am		2:00pm
	8:00am		3:00pm
	9:00am		4:00pm
	10:00am		5:00pm
	11:00am		6:00pm
	12:00pm		7:00pm

Daily Prayer List (Before you go to sleep tonight, who in your life requires prayer or what circumstance requires prayer today?)

1. _____   2. _____

3. _____   4. _____

Prayer Focus: Exodus 9:16   Date: _____

But I have raised you up for this very purpose, that I might show you my power and that my name might be proclaimed in all the earth.

How does this verse speak to your soul, heart, and mind?

_____

_____

_____

Daily Gratitude Prayer *(Consider a prayer like the following each morning before you start your day: Lord, thank you for this day. Lord, I am grateful for my health. Lord, thank you for trusting me to serve your people.)*

_____

_____

_____

Spend Time with God *(How did you spend time with God today? Did you pray, read scripture, or share His word with someone?)*

Daily Activity	Time	Daily Activity	Time
	6:00am		1:00pm
	7:00am		2:00pm
	8:00am		3:00pm
	9:00am		4:00pm
	10:00am		5:00pm
	11:00am		6:00pm
	12:00pm		7:00pm

Daily Prayer List *(Before you go to sleep tonight, who in your life requires prayer or what circumstance requires prayer today?)*

1. _____   2. _____

3. _____   4. _____

Prayer Focus: Philippians 1:6　　　　Date: _____

Being confident of this, that he who began a good work in you will carry it on to completion until the day of Christ Jesus.

How does this verse speak to your soul, heart, and mind?

_____

_____

_____

Daily Gratitude Prayer *(Consider a prayer like the following each morning before you start your day: Lord, thank you for this day. Lord, I am grateful for my health. Lord, thank you for trusting me to serve your people.)*

_____

_____

_____

Spend Time with God *(How did you spend time with God today? Did you pray, read scripture, or share His word with someone?)*

Daily Activity	Time	Daily Activity	Time
	6:00am		1:00pm
	7:00am		2:00pm
	8:00am		3:00pm
	9:00am		4:00pm
	10:00am		5:00pm
	11:00am		6:00pm
	12:00pm		7:00pm

Daily Prayer List *(Before you go to sleep tonight, who in your life requires prayer or what circumstance requires prayer today?)*

1. _____　　　2. _____

3. _____　　　4. _____

Prayer Focus: 1 Timothy 4:15

Date: _____

Be diligent in these matters; give yourself wholly to them, so that everyone may see your progress.

How does this verse speak to your soul, heart, and mind?

_____

_____

_____

Daily Gratitude Prayer *(Consider a prayer like the following each morning before you start your day: Lord, thank you for this day. Lord, I am grateful for my health. Lord, thank you for trusting me to serve your people.)*

_____

_____

_____

Spend Time with God *(How did you spend time with God today? Did you pray, read scripture, or share His word with someone?)*

Daily Activity	Time	Daily Activity	Time
	6:00am		1:00pm
	7:00am		2:00pm
	8:00am		3:00pm
	9:00am		4:00pm
	10:00am		5:00pm
	11:00am		6:00pm
	12:00pm		7:00pm

Daily Prayer List *(Before you go to sleep tonight, who in your life requires prayer or what circumstance requires prayer today?)*

1. _____   2. _____

3. _____   4. _____

Prayer Focus: 1 Peter 5:7 (KJV)   Date: _____

Casting all your care upon him; for he cares for you.

How does this verse speak to your soul, heart, and mind?

_____

_____

_____

Daily Gratitude Prayer *(Consider a prayer like the following each morning before you start your day: Lord, thank you for this day. Lord, I am grateful for my health. Lord, thank you for trusting me to serve your people.)*

_____

_____

_____

Spend Time with God *(How did you spend time with God today? Did you pray, read scripture, or share His word with someone?)*

Daily Activity	Time	Daily Activity	Time
	6:00am		1:00pm
	7:00am		2:00pm
	8:00am		3:00pm
	9:00am		4:00pm
	10:00am		5:00pm
	11:00am		6:00pm
	12:00pm		7:00pm

Daily Prayer List (Before you go to sleep tonight, who in your life requires prayer or what circumstance requires prayer today?)

1. _____   2. _____

3. _____   4. _____

Prayer Focus: James 4:8a   Date: _____

Come near to God and he will come near to you.

How does this verse speak to your soul, heart, and mind?

_____

_____

_____

Daily Gratitude Prayer *(Consider a prayer like the following each morning before you start your day: Lord, thank you for this day. Lord, I am grateful for my health. Lord, thank you for trusting me to serve your people.)*

_____

_____

_____

Spend Time with God *(How did you spend time with God today? Did you pray, read scripture, or share His word with someone?)*

Daily Activity	Time	Daily Activity	Time
	6:00am		1:00pm
	7:00am		2:00pm
	8:00am		3:00pm
	9:00am		4:00pm
	10:00am		5:00pm
	11:00am		6:00pm
	12:00pm		7:00pm

Daily Prayer List (Before you go to sleep tonight, who in your life requires prayer or what circumstance requires prayer today?)

1. _____   2. _____

3. _____   4. _____

Prayer Focus: 2 Timothy 1:7   Date: _____

For God has not given us a spirit of fear and timidity, but of power, love, and self-discipline.

How does this verse speak to your soul, heart, and mind?

_____

_____

_____

Daily Gratitude Prayer *(Consider a prayer like the following each morning before you start your day: Lord, thank you for this day. Lord, I am grateful for my health. Lord, thank you for trusting me to serve your people.)*

_____

_____

_____

Spend Time with God *(How did you spend time with God today? Did you pray, read scripture, or share His word with someone?)*

Daily Activity	Time	Daily Activity	Time
	6:00am		1:00pm
	7:00am		2:00pm
	8:00am		3:00pm
	9:00am		4:00pm
	10:00am		5:00pm
	11:00am		6:00pm
	12:00pm		7:00pm

Daily Prayer List *(Before you go to sleep tonight, who in your life requires prayer or what circumstance requires prayer today?)*

1. _____   2. _____

3. _____   4. _____

Prayer Focus: Psalm 59:16   Date: _____

But I will sing of your strength, in the morning I will sing of your love; for you are my fortress, my refuge in times of trouble.

How does this verse speak to your soul, heart, and mind?

_____

_____

_____

Daily Gratitude Prayer *(Consider a prayer like the following each morning before you start your day: Lord, thank you for this day. Lord, I am grateful for my health. Lord, thank you for trusting me to serve your people.)*

_____

_____

_____

Spend Time with God *(How did you spend time with God today? Did you pray, read scripture, or share His word with someone?)*

Daily Activity	Time	Daily Activity	Time
	6:00am		1:00pm
	7:00am		2:00pm
	8:00am		3:00pm
	9:00am		4:00pm
	10:00am		5:00pm
	11:00am		6:00pm
	12:00pm		7:00pm

Daily Prayer List *(Before you go to sleep tonight, who in your life requires prayer or what circumstance requires prayer today?)*

1. _____   2. _____

3. _____   4. _____

Prayer Focus: Philippians 4:19   Date: _____

And my God will meet all your needs according to the riches of his glory in Christ Jesus.

How does this verse speak to your soul, heart, and mind?

_____

_____

_____

Daily Gratitude Prayer *(Consider a prayer like the following each morning before you start your day: Lord, thank you for this day. Lord, I am grateful for my health. Lord, thank you for trusting me to serve your people.)*

_____

_____

_____

Spend Time with God *(How did you spend time with God today? Did you pray, read scripture, or share His word with someone?)*

Daily Activity	Time	Daily Activity	Time
	6:00am		1:00pm
	7:00am		2:00pm
	8:00am		3:00pm
	9:00am		4:00pm
	10:00am		5:00pm
	11:00am		6:00pm
	12:00pm		7:00pm

Daily Prayer List *(Before you go to sleep tonight, who in your life requires prayer or what circumstance requires prayer today?)*

1. _____   2. _____

3. _____   4. _____

Prayer Focus: Psalm 9:1   Date: _____

I will praise you, LORD, with all my heart; I will tell of all the marvelous things you have done.

How does this verse speak to your soul, heart, and mind?

_____

_____

_____

Daily Gratitude Prayer *(Consider a prayer like the following each morning before you start your day: Lord, thank you for this day. Lord, I am grateful for my health. Lord, thank you for trusting me to serve your people.)*

_____

_____

_____

Spend Time with God *(How did you spend time with God today? Did you pray, read scripture, or share His word with someone?)*

Daily Activity	Time	Daily Activity	Time
	6:00am		1:00pm
	7:00am		2:00pm
	8:00am		3:00pm
	9:00am		4:00pm
	10:00am		5:00pm
	11:00am		6:00pm
	12:00pm		7:00pm

Daily Prayer List *(Before you go to sleep tonight, who in your life requires prayer or what circumstance requires prayer today?)*

1. _____   2. _____

3. _____   4. _____

Prayer Focus: 1 Corinthians 3:16　　　　Date: _____

Don't you know that you yourselves are God's temple and that God's Spirit dwells in your midst?

How does this verse speak to your soul, heart, and mind?

_____

_____

_____

Daily Gratitude Prayer *(Consider a prayer like the following each morning before you start your day: Lord, thank you for this day. Lord, I am grateful for my health. Lord, thank you for trusting me to serve your people.)*

_____

_____

_____

Spend Time with God *(How did you spend time with God today? Did you pray, read scripture, or share His word with someone?)*

Daily Activity	Time	Daily Activity	Time
	6:00am		1:00pm
	7:00am		2:00pm
	8:00am		3:00pm
	9:00am		4:00pm
	10:00am		5:00pm
	11:00am		6:00pm
	12:00pm		7:00pm

Daily Prayer List *(Before you go to sleep tonight, who in your life requires prayer or what circumstance requires prayer today?)*

1. _____　　2. _____

3. _____　　4. _____

Prayer Focus: Psalm 4:8   Date: _____

In peace I will lie down and sleep, for you alone, LORD, make me dwell in safety.

How does this verse speak to your soul, heart, and mind?

_____

_____

_____

Daily Gratitude Prayer *(Consider a prayer like the following each morning before you start your day: Lord, thank you for this day. Lord, I am grateful for my health. Lord, thank you for trusting me to serve your people.)*

_____

_____

_____

Spend Time with God *(How did you spend time with God today? Did you pray, read scripture, or share His word with someone?)*

Daily Activity	Time	Daily Activity	Time
	6:00am		1:00pm
	7:00am		2:00pm
	8:00am		3:00pm
	9:00am		4:00pm
	10:00am		5:00pm
	11:00am		6:00pm
	12:00pm		7:00pm

Daily Prayer List *(Before you go to sleep tonight, who in your life requires prayer or what circumstance requires prayer today?)*

1. _____   2. _____

3. _____   4. _____

Prayer Focus: Ephesians 6:18   Date: _____

And pray in the Spirit on all occasions with all kinds of prayers and requests. With this in mind, be alert and always keep on praying for all the Lord's people.

How does this verse speak to your soul, heart, and mind?

_____

_____

_____

Daily Gratitude Prayer *(Consider a prayer like the following each morning before you start your day: Lord, thank you for this day. Lord, I am grateful for my health. Lord, thank you for trusting me to serve your people.)*

_____

_____

_____

Spend Time with God *(How did you spend time with God today? Did you pray, read scripture, or share His word with someone?)*

Daily Activity	Time	Daily Activity	Time
	6:00am		1:00pm
	7:00am		2:00pm
	8:00am		3:00pm
	9:00am		4:00pm
	10:00am		5:00pm
	11:00am		6:00pm
	12:00pm		7:00pm

Daily Prayer List *(Before you go to sleep tonight, who in your life requires prayer or what circumstance requires prayer today?)*

1. _____   2. _____

3. _____   4. _____

Prayer Focus: Matthew 10:31

Date: _____

So don't be afraid; you are worth more than many sparrows.

How does this verse speak to your soul, heart, and mind?

_____

_____

_____

Daily Gratitude Prayer *(Consider a prayer like the following each morning before you start your day: Lord, thank you for this day. Lord, I am grateful for my health. Lord, thank you for trusting me to serve your people.)*

_____

_____

_____

Spend Time with God *(How did you spend time with God today? Did you pray, read scripture, or share His word with someone?)*

Daily Activity	Time	Daily Activity	Time
	6:00am		1:00pm
	7:00am		2:00pm
	8:00am		3:00pm
	9:00am		4:00pm
	10:00am		5:00pm
	11:00am		6:00pm
	12:00pm		7:00pm

Daily Prayer List (Before you go to sleep tonight, who in your life requires prayer or what circumstance requires prayer today?)

1. _____

2. _____

3. _____

4. _____

Prayer Focus: Romans 12:12

Date: _____

Be joyful in hope, patient in affliction, faithful in prayer.

How does this verse speak to your soul, heart, and mind?

_____

_____

_____

Daily Gratitude Prayer *(Consider a prayer like the following each morning before you start your day: Lord, thank you for this day. Lord, I am grateful for my health. Lord, thank you for trusting me to serve your people.)*

_____

_____

_____

Spend Time with God *(How did you spend time with God today? Did you pray, read scripture, or share His word with someone?)*

Daily Activity	Time	Daily Activity	Time
	6:00am		1:00pm
	7:00am		2:00pm
	8:00am		3:00pm
	9:00am		4:00pm
	10:00am		5:00pm
	11:00am		6:00pm
	12:00pm		7:00pm

Daily Prayer List *(Before you go to sleep tonight, who in your life requires prayer or what circumstance requires prayer today?)*

1. _____   2. _____

3. _____   4. _____

Prayer Focus: James 1:22   Date: _____

Do not merely listen to the word, and so deceive yourselves. Do what it says.

How does this verse speak to your soul, heart, and mind?

_____

_____

_____

Daily Gratitude Prayer *(Consider a prayer like the following each morning before you start your day: Lord, thank you for this day. Lord, I am grateful for my health. Lord, thank you for trusting me to serve your people.)*

_____

_____

_____

Spend Time with God *(How did you spend time with God today? Did you pray, read scripture, or share His word with someone?)*

Daily Activity	Time	Daily Activity	Time
	6:00am		1:00pm
	7:00am		2:00pm
	8:00am		3:00pm
	9:00am		4:00pm
	10:00am		5:00pm
	11:00am		6:00pm
	12:00pm		7:00pm

Daily Prayer List *(Before you go to sleep tonight, who in your life requires prayer or what circumstance requires prayer today?)*

1. _____   2. _____

3. _____   4. _____

Prayer Focus: Psalm 37:16   Date: _____

Better is the little of the righteous Than the abundance of many wicked.

How does this verse speak to your soul, heart, and mind?

_____

_____

_____

Daily Gratitude Prayer *(Consider a prayer like the following each morning before you start your day: Lord, thank you for this day. Lord, I am grateful for my health. Lord, thank you for trusting me to serve your people.)*

_____

_____

_____

Spend Time with God *(How did you spend time with God today? Did you pray, read scripture, or share His word with someone?)*

Daily Activity	Time	Daily Activity	Time
	6:00am		1:00pm
	7:00am		2:00pm
	8:00am		3:00pm
	9:00am		4:00pm
	10:00am		5:00pm
	11:00am		6:00pm
	12:00pm		7:00pm

Daily Prayer List (Before you go to sleep tonight, who in your life requires prayer or what circumstance requires prayer today?)

1. _____   2. _____

3. _____   4. _____

Prayer Focus: Psalm 94:19   Date: _____

When the cares of my heart, are many, your consolations cheer my soul.

How does this verse speak to your soul, heart, and mind?

_____

_____

_____

Daily Gratitude Prayer *(Consider a prayer like the following each morning before you start your day: Lord, thank you for this day. Lord, I am grateful for my health. Lord, thank you for trusting me to serve your people.)*

_____

_____

_____

Spend Time with God *(How did you spend time with God today? Did you pray, read scripture, or share His word with someone?)*

Daily Activity	Time	Daily Activity	Time
	6:00am		1:00pm
	7:00am		2:00pm
	8:00am		3:00pm
	9:00am		4:00pm
	10:00am		5:00pm
	11:00am		6:00pm
	12:00pm		7:00pm

Daily Prayer List *(Before you go to sleep tonight, who in your life requires prayer or what circumstance requires prayer today?)*

1. _____   2. _____

3. _____   4. _____

Prayer Focus: Colossians 1:17 (BLB)   Date: _____

And He is before all things, and in Him all things hold together.

How does this verse speak to your soul, heart, and mind?

_____

_____

_____

Daily Gratitude Prayer *(Consider a prayer like the following each morning before you start your day: Lord, thank you for this day. Lord, I am grateful for my health. Lord, thank you for trusting me to serve your people.)*

_____

_____

_____

Spend Time with God *(How did you spend time with God today? Did you pray, read scripture, or share His word with someone?)*

Daily Activity	Time	Daily Activity	Time
	6:00am		1:00pm
	7:00am		2:00pm
	8:00am		3:00pm
	9:00am		4:00pm
	10:00am		5:00pm
	11:00am		6:00pm
	12:00pm		7:00pm

Daily Prayer List *(Before you go to sleep tonight, who in your life requires prayer or what circumstance requires prayer today?)*

1. _____   2. _____

3. _____   4. _____

Prayer Focus: 2 Corinthians 8:11   Date: _____

Now finish the work, so that your eager willingness to do it may be matched by your completion of it, according to your means.

How does this verse speak to your soul, heart, and mind?

_____

_____

_____

Daily Gratitude Prayer *(Consider a prayer like the following each morning before you start your day: Lord, thank you for this day. Lord, I am grateful for my health. Lord, thank you for trusting me to serve your people.)*

_____

_____

_____

Spend Time with God *(How did you spend time with God today? Did you pray, read scripture, or share His word with someone?)*

Daily Activity	Time	Daily Activity	Time
	6:00am		1:00pm
	7:00am		2:00pm
	8:00am		3:00pm
	9:00am		4:00pm
	10:00am		5:00pm
	11:00am		6:00pm
	12:00pm		7:00pm

Daily Prayer List *(Before you go to sleep tonight, who in your life requires prayer or what circumstance requires prayer today?)*

5. _____   6. _____

7. _____   8. _____

Prayer Focus: Romans 15:5   Date: _____

May the God who gives endurance and encouragement give you the same attitude of mind toward each other that Christ Jesus had

How does this verse speak to your soul, heart, and mind?

_____

_____

_____

Daily Gratitude Prayer *(Consider a prayer like the following each morning before you start your day: Lord, thank you for this day. Lord, I am grateful for my health. Lord, thank you for trusting me to serve your people.)*

_____

_____

_____

Spend Time with God *(How did you spend time with God today? Did you pray, read scripture, or share His word with someone?)*

Daily Activity	Time	Daily Activity	Time
	6:00am		1:00pm
	7:00am		2:00pm
	8:00am		3:00pm
	9:00am		4:00pm
	10:00am		5:00pm
	11:00am		6:00pm
	12:00pm		7:00pm

Daily Prayer List *(Before you go to sleep tonight, who in your life requires prayer or what circumstance requires prayer today?)*

1. _____   2. _____

3. _____   4. _____

Prayer Focus: Psalm 51:10   Date: _____

Create in me a pure heart, O God, and renew a steadfast spirit within me.

How does this verse speak to your soul, heart, and mind?

_____

_____

_____

Daily Gratitude Prayer *(Consider a prayer like the following each morning before you start your day: Lord, thank you for this day. Lord, I am grateful for my health. Lord, thank you for trusting me to serve your people.)*

_____

_____

_____

Spend Time with God *(How did you spend time with God today? Did you pray, read scripture, or share His word with someone?)*

Daily Activity	Time	Daily Activity	Time
	6:00am		1:00pm
	7:00am		2:00pm
	8:00am		3:00pm
	9:00am		4:00pm
	10:00am		5:00pm
	11:00am		6:00pm
	12:00pm		7:00pm

Daily Prayer List (Before you go to sleep tonight, who in your life requires prayer or what circumstance requires prayer today?)

1. _____   2. _____

3. _____   4. _____

Prayer Focus: Colossians 3:13　　　　Date: _____

Bear with each other and forgive one another if any of you has a grievance against someone. Forgive as the Lord forgave you.

How does this verse speak to your soul, heart, and mind?

_____

_____

_____

Daily Gratitude Prayer *(Consider a prayer like the following each morning before you start your day: Lord, thank you for this day. Lord, I am grateful for my health. Lord, thank you for trusting me to serve your people.)*

_____

_____

_____

Spend Time with God *(How did you spend time with God today? Did you pray, read scripture, or share His word with someone?)*

Daily Activity	Time	Daily Activity	Time
	6:00am		1:00pm
	7:00am		2:00pm
	8:00am		3:00pm
	9:00am		4:00pm
	10:00am		5:00pm
	11:00am		6:00pm
	12:00pm		7:00pm

Daily Prayer List *(Before you go to sleep tonight, who in your life requires prayer or what circumstance requires prayer today?)*

1. _____　　2. _____

3. _____　　4. _____

Prayer Focus: Proverbs 27:17   Date: _____

As iron sharpens iron, so a man sharpens the countenance of his friend.

How does this verse speak to your soul, heart, and mind?

_____

_____

_____

Daily Gratitude Prayer *(Consider a prayer like the following each morning before you start your day: Lord, thank you for this day. Lord, I am grateful for my health. Lord, thank you for trusting me to serve your people.)*

_____

_____

_____

Spend Time with God *(How did you spend time with God today? Did you pray, read scripture, or share His word with someone?)*

Daily Activity	Time	Daily Activity	Time
	6:00am		1:00pm
	7:00am		2:00pm
	8:00am		3:00pm
	9:00am		4:00pm
	10:00am		5:00pm
	11:00am		6:00pm
	12:00pm		7:00pm

Daily Prayer List *(Before you go to sleep tonight, who in your life requires prayer or what circumstance requires prayer today?)*

1. _____   2. _____

3. _____   4. _____

Prayer Focus: Psalm 8:4   Date: _____

What is man that You are mindful of him, And the son of man that You visit him?

How does this verse speak to your soul, heart, and mind?

_____

_____

_____

Daily Gratitude Prayer *(Consider a prayer like the following each morning before you start your day: Lord, thank you for this day. Lord, I am grateful for my health. Lord, thank you for trusting me to serve your people.)*

_____

_____

_____

Spend Time with God *(How did you spend time with God today? Did you pray, read scripture, or share His word with someone?)*

Daily Activity	Time	Daily Activity	Time
	6:00am		1:00pm
	7:00am		2:00pm
	8:00am		3:00pm
	9:00am		4:00pm
	10:00am		5:00pm
	11:00am		6:00pm
	12:00pm		7:00pm

Daily Prayer List (Before you go to sleep tonight, who in your life requires prayer or what circumstance requires prayer today?)

1. _____   2. _____

3. _____   4. _____

Prayer Focus: Isaiah 26:3   Date: _____

You will keep in perfect peace those whose minds are steadfast, because they trust in you.

How does this verse speak to your soul, heart, and mind?

_____

_____

_____

Daily Gratitude Prayer *(Consider a prayer like the following each morning before you start your day: Lord, thank you for this day. Lord, I am grateful for my health. Lord, thank you for trusting me to serve your people.)*

_____

_____

_____

Spend Time with God *(How did you spend time with God today? Did you pray, read scripture, or share His word with someone?)*

Daily Activity	Time	Daily Activity	Time
	6:00am		1:00pm
	7:00am		2:00pm
	8:00am		3:00pm
	9:00am		4:00pm
	10:00am		5:00pm
	11:00am		6:00pm
	12:00pm		7:00pm

Daily Prayer List *(Before you go to sleep tonight, who in your life requires prayer or what circumstance requires prayer today?)*

1. _____   2. _____

3. _____   4. _____

Prayer Focus: 1 Thessalonians 4:4   Date: _____

That each of you should learn to control your own body in a way that is holy and honorable.

How does this verse speak to your soul, heart, and mind?

_____

_____

_____

Daily Gratitude Prayer *(Consider a prayer like the following each morning before you start your day: Lord, thank you for this day. Lord, I am grateful for my health. Lord, thank you for trusting me to serve your people.)*

_____

_____

_____

Spend Time with God *(How did you spend time with God today? Did you pray, read scripture, or share His word with someone?)*

Daily Activity	Time	Daily Activity	Time
	6:00am		1:00pm
	7:00am		2:00pm
	8:00am		3:00pm
	9:00am		4:00pm
	10:00am		5:00pm
	11:00am		6:00pm
	12:00pm		7:00pm

Daily Prayer List *(Before you go to sleep tonight, who in your life requires prayer or what circumstance requires prayer today?)*

1. _____   2. _____

3. _____   4. _____

Prayer Focus: Proverbs 18:16   Date: _____

A man's gift makes room for him and brings him before great men.

How does this verse speak to your soul, heart, and mind?

_____

_____

_____

Daily Gratitude Prayer *(Consider a prayer like the following each morning before you start your day: Lord, thank you for this day. Lord, I am grateful for my health. Lord, thank you for trusting me to serve your people.)*

_____

_____

_____

Spend Time with God *(How did you spend time with God today? Did you pray, read scripture, or share His word with someone?)*

Daily Activity	Time	Daily Activity	Time
	6:00am		1:00pm
	7:00am		2:00pm
	8:00am		3:00pm
	9:00am		4:00pm
	10:00am		5:00pm
	11:00am		6:00pm
	12:00pm		7:00pm

Daily Prayer List (Before you go to sleep tonight, who in your life requires prayer or what circumstance requires prayer today?)

1. _____   2. _____

3. _____   4. _____

Prayer Focus: Psalm 55:6   Date: _____

I said, "Oh, that I had the wings of a dove! I would fly away and be at rest.

How does this verse speak to your soul, heart, and mind?

_____

_____

_____

Daily Gratitude Prayer *(Consider a prayer like the following each morning before you start your day: Lord, thank you for this day. Lord, I am grateful for my health. Lord, thank you for trusting me to serve your people.)*

_____

_____

_____

Spend Time with God *(How did you spend time with God today? Did you pray, read scripture, or share His word with someone?)*

Daily Activity	Time	Daily Activity	Time
	6:00am		1:00pm
	7:00am		2:00pm
	8:00am		3:00pm
	9:00am		4:00pm
	10:00am		5:00pm
	11:00am		6:00pm
	12:00pm		7:00pm

Daily Prayer List *(Before you go to sleep tonight, who in your life requires prayer or what circumstance requires prayer today?)*

1. _____   2. _____

3. _____   4. _____

Prayer Focus: 1 John 5:15   Date: _____

And if we know that he hears us—whatever we ask—we know that we have what we asked of him.

How does this verse speak to your soul, heart, and mind?

_____

_____

_____

Daily Gratitude Prayer *(Consider a prayer like the following each morning before you start your day: Lord, thank you for this day. Lord, I am grateful for my health. Lord, thank you for trusting me to serve your people.)*

_____

_____

_____

Spend Time with God *(How did you spend time with God today? Did you pray, read scripture, or share His word with someone?)*

Daily Activity	Time	Daily Activity	Time
	6:00am		1:00pm
	7:00am		2:00pm
	8:00am		3:00pm
	9:00am		4:00pm
	10:00am		5:00pm
	11:00am		6:00pm
	12:00pm		7:00pm

Daily Prayer List *(Before you go to sleep tonight, who in your life requires prayer or what circumstance requires prayer today?)*

1. _____   2. _____

3. _____   4. _____

Prayer Focus: Proverbs 18:15   Date: _____

The heart of the discerning acquires knowledge, for the ears of the wise seek it out.

How does this verse speak to your soul, heart, and mind?

_____

_____

_____

Daily Gratitude Prayer *(Consider a prayer like the following each morning before you start your day: Lord, thank you for this day. Lord, I am grateful for my health. Lord, thank you for trusting me to serve your people.)*

_____

_____

_____

Spend Time with God *(How did you spend time with God today? Did you pray, read scripture, or share His word with someone?)*

Daily Activity	Time	Daily Activity	Time
	6:00am		1:00pm
	7:00am		2:00pm
	8:00am		3:00pm
	9:00am		4:00pm
	10:00am		5:00pm
	11:00am		6:00pm
	12:00pm		7:00pm

Daily Prayer List *(Before you go to sleep tonight, who in your life requires prayer or what circumstance requires prayer today?)*

1. _____   2. _____

3. _____   4. _____

Prayer Focus: 1 Timothy 4:14   Date: _____

Do not neglect your gift, which was given you through prophecy when the body of elders laid their hands on you.

How does this verse speak to your soul, heart, and mind?

_____

_____

_____

Daily Gratitude Prayer *(Consider a prayer like the following each morning before you start your day: Lord, thank you for this day. Lord, I am grateful for my health. Lord, thank you for trusting me to serve your people.)*

_____

_____

_____

Spend Time with God *(How did you spend time with God today? Did you pray, read scripture, or share His word with someone?)*

Daily Activity	Time	Daily Activity	Time
	6:00am		1:00pm
	7:00am		2:00pm
	8:00am		3:00pm
	9:00am		4:00pm
	10:00am		5:00pm
	11:00am		6:00pm
	12:00pm		7:00pm

Daily Prayer List *(Before you go to sleep tonight, who in your life requires prayer or what circumstance requires prayer today?)*

1. _____   2. _____

3. _____   4. _____

Prayer Focus: Psalm55:22   Date: _____

Cast your cares on the LORD and he will sustain you; he will never let the righteous be shaken.

How does this verse speak to your soul, heart, and mind?

_____

_____

_____

Daily Gratitude Prayer *(Consider a prayer like the following each morning before you start your day: Lord, thank you for this day. Lord, I am grateful for my health. Lord, thank you for trusting me to serve your people.)*

_____

_____

_____

Spend Time with God *(How did you spend time with God today? Did you pray, read scripture, or share His word with someone?)*

Daily Activity	Time	Daily Activity	Time
	6:00am		1:00pm
	7:00am		2:00pm
	8:00am		3:00pm
	9:00am		4:00pm
	10:00am		5:00pm
	11:00am		6:00pm
	12:00pm		7:00pm

Daily Prayer List *(Before you go to sleep tonight, who in your life requires prayer or what circumstance requires prayer today?)*

1. _____   2. _____

3. _____   4. _____

Prayer Focus: Exodus 35:10   Date: _____

All who are skilled among you are to come and make everything the LORD has commanded.

How does this verse speak to your soul, heart, and mind?

_____

_____

_____

Daily Gratitude Prayer *(Consider a prayer like the following each morning before you start your day: Lord, thank you for this day. Lord, I am grateful for my health. Lord, thank you for trusting me to serve your people.)*

_____

_____

_____

Spend Time with God *(How did you spend time with God today? Did you pray, read scripture, or share His word with someone?)*

Daily Activity	Time	Daily Activity	Time
	6:00am		1:00pm
	7:00am		2:00pm
	8:00am		3:00pm
	9:00am		4:00pm
	10:00am		5:00pm
	11:00am		6:00pm
	12:00pm		7:00pm

Daily Prayer List *(Before you go to sleep tonight, who in your life requires prayer or what circumstance requires prayer today?)*

1. _____   2. _____

3. _____   4. _____

Prayer Focus: Romans 15:13   Date: _____

May the God of hope fill you with all joy and peace as you trust in him, so that you may overflow with hope by the power of the Holy Spirit.

How does this verse speak to your soul, heart, and mind?

_____

_____

_____

Daily Gratitude Prayer *(Consider a prayer like the following each morning before you start your day: Lord, thank you for this day. Lord, I am grateful for my health. Lord, thank you for trusting me to serve your people.)*

_____

_____

_____

Spend Time with God *(How did you spend time with God today? Did you pray, read scripture, or share His word with someone?)*

Daily Activity	Time	Daily Activity	Time
	6:00am		1:00pm
	7:00am		2:00pm
	8:00am		3:00pm
	9:00am		4:00pm
	10:00am		5:00pm
	11:00am		6:00pm
	12:00pm		7:00pm

Daily Prayer List *(Before you go to sleep tonight, who in your life requires prayer or what circumstance requires prayer today?)*

1. _____   2. _____

3. _____   4. _____

Prayer Focus: 1 Corinthians 15:57   Date: _____

But thanks be to God! He gives us the victory through our Lord Jesus Christ.

How does this verse speak to your soul, heart, and mind?

_____

_____

_____

Daily Gratitude Prayer *(Consider a prayer like the following each morning before you start your day: Lord, thank you for this day. Lord, I am grateful for my health. Lord, thank you for trusting me to serve your people.)*

_____

_____

_____

Spend Time with God *(How did you spend time with God today? Did you pray, read scripture, or share His word with someone?)*

Daily Activity	Time	Daily Activity	Time
	6:00am		1:00pm
	7:00am		2:00pm
	8:00am		3:00pm
	9:00am		4:00pm
	10:00am		5:00pm
	11:00am		6:00pm
	12:00pm		7:00pm

Daily Prayer List *(Before you go to sleep tonight, who in your life requires prayer or what circumstance requires prayer today?)*

1. _____   2. _____

3. _____   4. _____

Prayer Focus: Matthew 21:22

Date: _____

If you believe, you will receive whatever you ask for in prayer.

How does this verse speak to your soul, heart, and mind?

_____

_____

_____

Daily Gratitude Prayer *(Consider a prayer like the following each morning before you start your day: Lord, thank you for this day. Lord, I am grateful for my health. Lord, thank you for trusting me to serve your people.)*

_____

_____

_____

Spend Time with God *(How did you spend time with God today? Did you pray, read scripture, or share His word with someone?)*

Daily Activity	Time	Daily Activity	Time
	6:00am		1:00pm
	7:00am		2:00pm
	8:00am		3:00pm
	9:00am		4:00pm
	10:00am		5:00pm
	11:00am		6:00pm
	12:00pm		7:00pm

Daily Prayer List *(Before you go to sleep tonight, who in your life requires prayer or what circumstance requires prayer today?)*

1. _____

2. _____

3. _____

4. _____

Prayer Focus: 1 Peter 4:10   Date: _____

Each of you should use whatever gift you have received to serve others, as faithful stewards of God's grace in its various forms.

How does this verse speak to your soul, heart, and mind?

_____

_____

_____

Daily Gratitude Prayer *(Consider a prayer like the following each morning before you start your day: Lord, thank you for this day. Lord, I am grateful for my health. Lord, thank you for trusting me to serve your people.)*

_____

_____

_____

Spend Time with God *(How did you spend time with God today? Did you pray, read scripture, or share His word with someone?)*

Daily Activity	Time	Daily Activity	Time
	6:00am		1:00pm
	7:00am		2:00pm
	8:00am		3:00pm
	9:00am		4:00pm
	10:00am		5:00pm
	11:00am		6:00pm
	12:00pm		7:00pm

Daily Prayer List *(Before you go to sleep tonight, who in your life requires prayer or what circumstance requires prayer today?)*

1. _____ 2. _____

3. _____ 4. _____

Prayer Focus: Luke 1:37   Date: _____

For no word from God will ever fail.

How does this verse speak to your soul, heart, and mind?

_____

_____

_____

Daily Gratitude Prayer *(Consider a prayer like the following each morning before you start your day: Lord, thank you for this day. Lord, I am grateful for my health. Lord, thank you for trusting me to serve your people.)*

_____

_____

_____

Spend Time with God *(How did you spend time with God today? Did you pray, read scripture, or share His word with someone?)*

Daily Activity	Time	Daily Activity	Time
	6:00am		1:00pm
	7:00am		2:00pm
	8:00am		3:00pm
	9:00am		4:00pm
	10:00am		5:00pm
	11:00am		6:00pm
	12:00pm		7:00pm

Daily Prayer List *(Before you go to sleep tonight, who in your life requires prayer or what circumstance requires prayer today?)*

1. _____   2. _____

3. _____   4. _____

Prayer Focus: Colossians 1:1   Date: _____

Being strengthened with all power according to his glorious might so that you may have great endurance and patience.

How does this verse speak to your soul, heart, and mind?

_____

_____

_____

Daily Gratitude Prayer *(Consider a prayer like the following each morning before you start your day: Lord, thank you for this day. Lord, I am grateful for my health. Lord, thank you for trusting me to serve your people.)*

_____

_____

_____

Spend Time with God *(How did you spend time with God today? Did you pray, read scripture, or share His word with someone?)*

Daily Activity	Time	Daily Activity	Time
	6:00am		1:00pm
	7:00am		2:00pm
	8:00am		3:00pm
	9:00am		4:00pm
	10:00am		5:00pm
	11:00am		6:00pm
	12:00pm		7:00pm

Daily Prayer List *(Before you go to sleep tonight, who in your life requires prayer or what circumstance requires prayer today?)*

1. _____   2. _____

3. _____   4. _____

Prayer Focus: Proverbs 19:17   Date: _____

Whoever is kind to the poor lends to the LORD, and he will reward them for what they have done.

How does this verse speak to your soul, heart, and mind?

_____

_____

_____

Daily Gratitude Prayer *(Consider a prayer like the following each morning before you start your day: Lord, thank you for this day. Lord, I am grateful for my health. Lord, thank you for trusting me to serve your people.)*

_____

_____

_____

Spend Time with God *(How did you spend time with God today? Did you pray, read scripture, or share His word with someone?)*

Daily Activity	Time	Daily Activity	Time
	6:00am		1:00pm
	7:00am		2:00pm
	8:00am		3:00pm
	9:00am		4:00pm
	10:00am		5:00pm
	11:00am		6:00pm
	12:00pm		7:00pm

Daily Prayer List *(Before you go to sleep tonight, who in your life requires prayer or what circumstance requires prayer today?)*

1. _____   2. _____

3. _____   4. _____

Prayer Focus: Isaiah 46:4   Date: _____

Even to your old age and gray hairs I am he, I am he who will sustain you. I have made you and I will carry you; I will sustain you and I will rescue you.

How does this verse speak to your soul, heart, and mind?

_____

_____

_____

Daily Gratitude Prayer *(Consider a prayer like the following each morning before you start your day: Lord, thank you for this day. Lord, I am grateful for my health. Lord, thank you for trusting me to serve your people.)*

_____

_____

_____

Spend Time with God *(How did you spend time with God today? Did you pray, read scripture, or share His word with someone?)*

Daily Activity	Time	Daily Activity	Time
	6:00am		1:00pm
	7:00am		2:00pm
	8:00am		3:00pm
	9:00am		4:00pm
	10:00am		5:00pm
	11:00am		6:00pm
	12:00pm		7:00pm

Daily Prayer List *(Before you go to sleep tonight, who in your life requires prayer or what circumstance requires prayer today?)*

1. _____   2. _____

3. _____   4. _____

Prayer Focus: Habakkuk 2:2   Date: _____

Write the vision and make it plain on tablets, that he may run who reads it.

How does this verse speak to your soul, heart, and mind?

_____

_____

_____

Daily Gratitude Prayer *(Consider a prayer like the following each morning before you start your day: Lord, thank you for this day. Lord, I am grateful for my health. Lord, thank you for trusting me to serve your people.)*

_____

_____

_____

Spend Time with God *(How did you spend time with God today? Did you pray, read scripture, or share His word with someone?)*

Daily Activity	Time	Daily Activity	Time
	6:00am		1:00pm
	7:00am		2:00pm
	8:00am		3:00pm
	9:00am		4:00pm
	10:00am		5:00pm
	11:00am		6:00pm
	12:00pm		7:00pm

Daily Prayer List (Before you go to sleep tonight, who in your life requires prayer or what circumstance requires prayer today?)

1. _____   2. _____

3. _____   4. _____

Prayer Focus: 1 Corinthians 9:24   Date: _____

Do you not know that in a race all the runners run, but only one gets the prize? Run in such a way as to get the prize.

How does this verse speak to your soul, heart, and mind?

_____

_____

_____

Daily Gratitude Prayer *(Consider a prayer like the following each morning before you start your day: Lord, thank you for this day. Lord, I am grateful for my health. Lord, thank you for trusting me to serve your people.)*

_____

_____

_____

Spend Time with God *(How did you spend time with God today? Did you pray, read scripture, or share His word with someone?)*

Daily Activity	Time	Daily Activity	Time
	6:00am		1:00pm
	7:00am		2:00pm
	8:00am		3:00pm
	9:00am		4:00pm
	10:00am		5:00pm
	11:00am		6:00pm
	12:00pm		7:00pm

Daily Prayer List *(Before you go to sleep tonight, who in your life requires prayer or what circumstance requires prayer today?)*

1. _____   2. _____

3. _____   4. _____

Prayer Focus: 2 Corinthians 4:18   Date: _____

So, we fix our eyes not on what is seen, but on what is unseen, since what is seen is temporary, but what is unseen is eternal.

How does this verse speak to your soul, heart, and mind?

_____

_____

_____

Daily Gratitude Prayer *(Consider a prayer like the following each morning before you start your day: Lord, thank you for this day. Lord, I am grateful for my health. Lord, thank you for trusting me to serve your people.)*

_____

_____

_____

Spend Time with God *(How did you spend time with God today? Did you pray, read scripture, or share His word with someone?)*

Daily Activity	Time	Daily Activity	Time
	6:00am		1:00pm
	7:00am		2:00pm
	8:00am		3:00pm
	9:00am		4:00pm
	10:00am		5:00pm
	11:00am		6:00pm
	12:00pm		7:00pm

Daily Prayer List *(Before you go to sleep tonight, who in your life requires prayer or what circumstance requires prayer today?)*

1. _____   2. _____

3. _____   4. _____

Prayer Focus: Lamentations 3:25   Date: _____

The LORD is good to those whose hope is in him, to the one who seeks him.

How does this verse speak to your soul, heart, and mind?

_____

_____

_____

Daily Gratitude Prayer *(Consider a prayer like the following each morning before you start your day: Lord, thank you for this day. Lord, I am grateful for my health. Lord, thank you for trusting me to serve your people.)*

_____

_____

_____

Spend Time with God *(How did you spend time with God today? Did you pray, read scripture, or share His word with someone?)*

Daily Activity	Time	Daily Activity	Time
	6:00am		1:00pm
	7:00am		2:00pm
	8:00am		3:00pm
	9:00am		4:00pm
	10:00am		5:00pm
	11:00am		6:00pm
	12:00pm		7:00pm

Daily Prayer List *(Before you go to sleep tonight, who in your life requires prayer or what circumstance requires prayer today?)*

1. _____   2. _____

3. _____   4. _____

Prayer Focus: John 1:16   Date: _____

Out of his fullness we have all received grace in place of grace already given.

How does this verse speak to your soul, heart, and mind?

_____

_____

_____

Daily Gratitude Prayer *(Consider a prayer like the following each morning before you start your day: Lord, thank you for this day. Lord, I am grateful for my health. Lord, thank you for trusting me to serve your people.)*

_____

_____

_____

Spend Time with God *(How did you spend time with God today? Did you pray, read scripture, or share His word with someone?)*

Daily Activity	Time	Daily Activity	Time
	6:00am		1:00pm
	7:00am		2:00pm
	8:00am		3:00pm
	9:00am		4:00pm
	10:00am		5:00pm
	11:00am		6:00pm
	12:00pm		7:00pm

Daily Prayer List (Before you go to sleep tonight, who in your life requires prayer or what circumstance requires prayer today?)

1. _____   2. _____

3. _____   4. _____

Prayer Focus: 1 Corinthians 6:20   Date: _____

You were bought at a price. Therefore, honor God with your bodies.

How does this verse speak to your soul, heart, and mind?

_____

_____

_____

Daily Gratitude Prayer *(Consider a prayer like the following each morning before you start your day: Lord, thank you for this day. Lord, I am grateful for my health. Lord, thank you for trusting me to serve your people.)*

_____

_____

_____

Spend Time with God *(How did you spend time with God today? Did you pray, read scripture, or share His word with someone?)*

Daily Activity	Time	Daily Activity	Time
	6:00am		1:00pm
	7:00am		2:00pm
	8:00am		3:00pm
	9:00am		4:00pm
	10:00am		5:00pm
	11:00am		6:00pm
	12:00pm		7:00pm

Daily Prayer List *(Before you go to sleep tonight, who in your life requires prayer or what circumstance requires prayer today?)*

1. _____   2. _____

3. _____   4. _____

Prayer Focus: 1 Peter 3:4   Date: _____

Rather let it be the hidden person of the heart, with the incorruptible beauty of a gentle and quiet spirit, which is very precious in the sight of God.

How does this verse speak to your soul, heart, and mind?

_____

_____

_____

Daily Gratitude Prayer *(Consider a prayer like the following each morning before you start your day: Lord, thank you for this day. Lord, I am grateful for my health. Lord, thank you for trusting me to serve your people.)*

_____

_____

_____

Spend Time with God *(How did you spend time with God today? Did you pray, read scripture, or share His word with someone?)*

Daily Activity	Time	Daily Activity	Time
	6:00am		1:00pm
	7:00am		2:00pm
	8:00am		3:00pm
	9:00am		4:00pm
	10:00am		5:00pm
	11:00am		6:00pm
	12:00pm		7:00pm

Daily Prayer List *(Before you go to sleep tonight, who in your life requires prayer or what circumstance requires prayer today?)*

1. _____   2. _____

3. _____   4. _____

Prayer Focus: Ecclesiastes 3:7   Date: _____

A time to tear and a time to mend, a time to be silent and a time to speak.

How does this verse speak to your soul, heart, and mind?

_____

_____

_____

Daily Gratitude Prayer *(Consider a prayer like the following each morning before you start your day: Lord, thank you for this day. Lord, I am grateful for my health. Lord, thank you for trusting me to serve your people.)*

_____

_____

_____

Spend Time with God *(How did you spend time with God today? Did you pray, read scripture, or share His word with someone?)*

Daily Activity	Time	Daily Activity	Time
	6:00am		1:00pm
	7:00am		2:00pm
	8:00am		3:00pm
	9:00am		4:00pm
	10:00am		5:00pm
	11:00am		6:00pm
	12:00pm		7:00pm

Daily Prayer List *(Before you go to sleep tonight, who in your life requires prayer or what circumstance requires prayer today?)*

1. _____   2. _____

3. _____   4. _____

Prayer Focus: Luke 10:19   Date: _____

Behold, I give you the authority to trample on serpents and scorpions, and over all the power of the enemy, and nothing shall by any means hurt you.

How does this verse speak to your soul, heart, and mind?

_____

_____

_____

Daily Gratitude Prayer *(Consider a prayer like the following each morning before you start your day: Lord, thank you for this day. Lord, I am grateful for my health. Lord, thank you for trusting me to serve your people.)*

_____

_____

_____

Spend Time with God *(How did you spend time with God today? Did you pray, read scripture, or share His word with someone?)*

Daily Activity	Time	Daily Activity	Time
	6:00am		1:00pm
	7:00am		2:00pm
	8:00am		3:00pm
	9:00am		4:00pm
	10:00am		5:00pm
	11:00am		6:00pm
	12:00pm		7:00pm

Daily Prayer List *(Before you go to sleep tonight, who in your life requires prayer or what circumstance requires prayer today?)*

1. _____   2. _____

3. _____   4. _____

Prayer Focus: Mark 11:23   Date: _____

For assuredly, I say to you, whoever says to this mountain, 'Be removed and be cast into the sea,' and does not doubt in his heart, but believes that those things he says will be done, he will have whatever he says.

How does this verse speak to your soul, heart, and mind?

_____

_____

_____

Daily Gratitude Prayer *(Consider a prayer like the following each morning before you start your day: Lord, thank you for this day. Lord, I am grateful for my health. Lord, thank you for trusting me to serve your people.)*

_____

_____

_____

Spend Time with God *(How did you spend time with God today? Did you pray, read scripture, or share His word with someone?)*

Daily Activity	Time	Daily Activity	Time
	6:00am		1:00pm
	7:00am		2:00pm
	8:00am		3:00pm
	9:00am		4:00pm
	10:00am		5:00pm
	11:00am		6:00pm
	12:00pm		7:00pm

Daily Prayer List *(Before you go to sleep tonight, who in your life requires prayer or what circumstance requires prayer today?)*

1. _____   2. _____

3. _____   4. _____

Prayer Focus: Luke 8:50   Date: _____

But when Jesus heard it, He answered him, saying, "Do not be afraid; only believe, and she will be made well."

How does this verse speak to your soul, heart, and mind?

_____

_____

_____

Daily Gratitude Prayer *(Consider a prayer like the following each morning before you start your day: Lord, thank you for this day. Lord, I am grateful for my health. Lord, thank you for trusting me to serve your people.)*

_____

_____

_____

Spend Time with God *(How did you spend time with God today? Did you pray, read scripture, or share His word with someone?)*

Daily Activity	Time	Daily Activity	Time
	6:00am		1:00pm
	7:00am		2:00pm
	8:00am		3:00pm
	9:00am		4:00pm
	10:00am		5:00pm
	11:00am		6:00pm
	12:00pm		7:00pm

Daily Prayer List (Before you go to sleep tonight, who in your life requires prayer or what circumstance requires prayer today?)

1. _____   2. _____

3. _____   4. _____

Prayer Focus: Joshua 1:9   Date: _____

Have I not commanded you? "Be strong and of good courage; do not be afraid, nor be dismayed, for the LORD your God is with you wherever you go."

How does this verse speak to your soul, heart, and mind?

_____

_____

_____

Daily Gratitude Prayer *(Consider a prayer like the following each morning before you start your day: Lord, thank you for this day. Lord, I am grateful for my health. Lord, thank you for trusting me to serve your people.)*

_____

_____

_____

Spend Time with God *(How did you spend time with God today? Did you pray, read scripture, or share His word with someone?)*

Daily Activity	Time	Daily Activity	Time
	6:00am		1:00pm
	7:00am		2:00pm
	8:00am		3:00pm
	9:00am		4:00pm
	10:00am		5:00pm
	11:00am		6:00pm
	12:00pm		7:00pm

Daily Prayer List (Before you go to sleep tonight, who in your life requires prayer or what circumstance requires prayer today?)

1. _____   2. _____

3. _____   4. _____

Prayer Focus: Isaiah 41:13   Date: _____

For I am the LORD your God who takes hold of your right hand and says to you, do not fear; I will help you.

How does this verse speak to your soul, heart, and mind?

_____

_____

_____

Daily Gratitude Prayer *(Consider a prayer like the following each morning before you start your day: Lord, thank you for this day. Lord, I am grateful for my health. Lord, thank you for trusting me to serve your people.)*

_____

_____

_____

Spend Time with God *(How did you spend time with God today? Did you pray, read scripture, or share His word with someone?)*

Daily Activity	Time	Daily Activity	Time
	6:00am		1:00pm
	7:00am		2:00pm
	8:00am		3:00pm
	9:00am		4:00pm
	10:00am		5:00pm
	11:00am		6:00pm
	12:00pm		7:00pm

Daily Prayer List *(Before you go to sleep tonight, who in your life requires prayer or what circumstance requires prayer today?)*

1. _____   2. _____

3. _____   4. _____

Prayer Focus: Colossians 1:11   Date: _____

Strengthened with all might, according to His glorious power, for all patience and longsuffering with joy. Giving thanks to the father who has qualified us to be partakers of the inheritance of the saints in the light.

How does this verse speak to your soul, heart, and mind?

_____

_____

_____

Daily Gratitude Prayer *(Consider a prayer like the following each morning before you start your day: Lord, thank you for this day. Lord, I am grateful for my health. Lord, thank you for trusting me to serve your people.)*

_____

_____

_____

Spend Time with God *(How did you spend time with God today? Did you pray, read scripture, or share His word with someone?)*

Daily Activity	Time	Daily Activity	Time
	6:00am		1:00pm
	7:00am		2:00pm
	8:00am		3:00pm
	9:00am		4:00pm
	10:00am		5:00pm
	11:00am		6:00pm
	12:00pm		7:00pm

Daily Prayer List *(Before you go to sleep tonight, who in your life requires prayer or what circumstance requires prayer today?)*

1. _____   2. _____

3. _____   4. _____

Prayer Focus: Philippians 4:13

Date: _____

I can do all things through Christ who strengthens me.

How does this verse speak to your soul, heart, and mind?

_____

_____

_____

Daily Gratitude Prayer *(Consider a prayer like the following each morning before you start your day: Lord, thank you for this day. Lord, I am grateful for my health. Lord, thank you for trusting me to serve your people.)*

_____

_____

_____

Spend Time with God *(How did you spend time with God today? Did you pray, read scripture, or share His word with someone?)*

Daily Activity	Time	Daily Activity	Time
	6:00am		1:00pm
	7:00am		2:00pm
	8:00am		3:00pm
	9:00am		4:00pm
	10:00am		5:00pm
	11:00am		6:00pm
	12:00pm		7:00pm

Daily Prayer List *(Before you go to sleep tonight, who in your life requires prayer or what circumstance requires prayer today?)*

1. _____

2. _____

3. _____

4. _____

Prayer Focus: Luke 1:45   Date: _____

"Blessed is she who has believed that the Lord would fulfill his promises to her!"

How does this verse speak to your soul, heart, and mind?

_____

_____

_____

Daily Gratitude Prayer *(Consider a prayer like the following each morning before you start your day: Lord, thank you for this day. Lord, I am grateful for my health. Lord, thank you for trusting me to serve your people.)*

_____

_____

_____

Spend Time with God *(How did you spend time with God today? Did you pray, read scripture, or share His word with someone?)*

Daily Activity	Time	Daily Activity	Time
	6:00am		1:00pm
	7:00am		2:00pm
	8:00am		3:00pm
	9:00am		4:00pm
	10:00am		5:00pm
	11:00am		6:00pm
	12:00pm		7:00pm

Daily Prayer List (Before you go to sleep tonight, who in your life requires prayer or what circumstance requires prayer today?)

1. _____   2. _____

3. _____   4. _____

Prayer Focus: Ephesians 6:11   Date: _____

Put on the full armor of God, so that you can take your stand against the devil's schemes.

How does this verse speak to your soul, heart, and mind?

_____

_____

_____

Daily Gratitude Prayer *(Consider a prayer like the following each morning before you start your day: Lord, thank you for this day. Lord, I am grateful for my health. Lord, thank you for trusting me to serve your people.)*

_____

_____

_____

Spend Time with God *(How did you spend time with God today? Did you pray, read scripture, or share His word with someone?)*

Daily Activity	Time	Daily Activity	Time
	6:00am		1:00pm
	7:00am		2:00pm
	8:00am		3:00pm
	9:00am		4:00pm
	10:00am		5:00pm
	11:00am		6:00pm
	12:00pm		7:00pm

Daily Prayer List *(Before you go to sleep tonight, who in your life requires prayer or what circumstance requires prayer today?)*

1. _____   2. _____

3. _____   4. _____

Prayer Focus: 1 Corinthians 9:24   Date: _____

Do you not know that those who run in a race all run, but one receives the prize? Run in such a way that you may obtain it.

How does this verse speak to your soul, heart, and mind?

_____

_____

_____

Daily Gratitude Prayer *(Consider a prayer like the following each morning before you start your day: Lord, thank you for this day. Lord, I am grateful for my health. Lord, thank you for trusting me to serve your people.)*

_____

_____

_____

Spend Time with God *(How did you spend time with God today? Did you pray, read scripture, or share His word with someone?)*

Daily Activity	Time	Daily Activity	Time
	6:00am		1:00pm
	7:00am		2:00pm
	8:00am		3:00pm
	9:00am		4:00pm
	10:00am		5:00pm
	11:00am		6:00pm
	12:00pm		7:00pm

Daily Prayer List *(Before you go to sleep tonight, who in your life requires prayer or what circumstance requires prayer today?)*

1. _____   2. _____

3. _____   4. _____

Prayer Focus: Isaiah 43:19   Date: _____

Behold, I will do a new thing, now it shall spring forth; Shall you not know it? I will even make a road in the wilderness and rivers in the desert.

How does this verse speak to your soul, heart, and mind?

_____

_____

_____

Daily Gratitude Prayer *(Consider a prayer like the following each morning before you start your day: Lord, thank you for this day. Lord, I am grateful for my health. Lord, thank you for trusting me to serve your people.)*

_____

_____

_____

Spend Time with God *(How did you spend time with God today? Did you pray, read scripture, or share His word with someone?)*

Daily Activity	Time	Daily Activity	Time
	6:00am		1:00pm
	7:00am		2:00pm
	8:00am		3:00pm
	9:00am		4:00pm
	10:00am		5:00pm
	11:00am		6:00pm
	12:00pm		7:00pm

Daily Prayer List *(Before you go to sleep tonight, who in your life requires prayer or what circumstance requires prayer today?)*

1. _____   2. _____

3. _____   4. _____

Prayer Focus: James 1:2-3   Date: _____

Consider it pure joy, my brothers, and sisters, whenever you face trials of many kinds. because you know that the testing of your faith produces perseverance.

How does this verse speak to your soul, heart, and mind?

_____

_____

_____

Daily Gratitude Prayer *(Consider a prayer like the following each morning before you start your day: Lord, thank you for this day. Lord, I am grateful for my health. Lord, thank you for trusting me to serve your people.)*

_____

_____

_____

Spend Time with God *(How did you spend time with God today? Did you pray, read scripture, or share His word with someone?)*

Daily Activity	Time	Daily Activity	Time
	6:00am		1:00pm
	7:00am		2:00pm
	8:00am		3:00pm
	9:00am		4:00pm
	10:00am		5:00pm
	11:00am		6:00pm
	12:00pm		7:00pm

Daily Prayer List *(Before you go to sleep tonight, who in your life requires prayer or what circumstance requires prayer today?)*

1. _____   2. _____

3. _____   4. _____

Prayer Focus: 2 Corinthians 8:11   Date: _____

Now finish the work, so that your eager willingness to do it may be matched by your completion of it, according to your means.

How does this verse speak to your soul, heart, and mind?

_____

_____

_____

Daily Gratitude Prayer *(Consider a prayer like the following each morning before you start your day: Lord, thank you for this day. Lord, I am grateful for my health. Lord, thank you for trusting me to serve your people.)*

_____

_____

_____

Spend Time with God *(How did you spend time with God today? Did you pray, read scripture, or share His word with someone?)*

Daily Activity	Time	Daily Activity	Time
	6:00am		1:00pm
	7:00am		2:00pm
	8:00am		3:00pm
	9:00am		4:00pm
	10:00am		5:00pm
	11:00am		6:00pm
	12:00pm		7:00pm

Daily Prayer List *(Before you go to sleep tonight, who in your life requires prayer or what circumstance requires prayer today?)*

1. _____   2. _____

3. _____   4. _____

Prayer Focus: 1 Corinthians 10:31   Date: _____

Therefore, whether you eat or drink, or whatever you do, do all to the glory of God.

How does this verse speak to your soul, heart, and mind?

_____

_____

_____

Daily Gratitude Prayer *(Consider a prayer like the following each morning before you start your day: Lord, thank you for this day. Lord, I am grateful for my health. Lord, thank you for trusting me to serve your people.)*

_____

_____

_____

Spend Time with God *(How did you spend time with God today? Did you pray, read scripture, or share His word with someone?)*

Daily Activity	Time	Daily Activity	Time
	6:00am		1:00pm
	7:00am		2:00pm
	8:00am		3:00pm
	9:00am		4:00pm
	10:00am		5:00pm
	11:00am		6:00pm
	12:00pm		7:00pm

Daily Prayer List *(Before you go to sleep tonight, who in your life requires prayer or what circumstance requires prayer today?)*

1. _____   2. _____

3. _____   4. _____

Prayer Focus: Proverbs 3:5-6   Date: _____

Trust in the LORD with all your heart and lean not on your own understanding; In all your ways acknowledge Him, And He shall direct your paths.

How does this verse speak to your soul, heart, and mind?

_____

_____

_____

Daily Gratitude Prayer *(Consider a prayer like the following each morning before you start your day: Lord, thank you for this day. Lord, I am grateful for my health. Lord, thank you for trusting me to serve your people.)*

_____

_____

_____

Spend Time with God *(How did you spend time with God today? Did you pray, read scripture, or share His word with someone?)*

Daily Activity	Time	Daily Activity	Time
	6:00am		1:00pm
	7:00am		2:00pm
	8:00am		3:00pm
	9:00am		4:00pm
	10:00am		5:00pm
	11:00am		6:00pm
	12:00pm		7:00pm

Daily Prayer List *(Before you go to sleep tonight, who in your life requires prayer or what circumstance requires prayer today?)*

1. _____   2. _____

3. _____   4. _____

Prayer Focus: Proverbs 16:3   Date: _____

Commit your works to the LORD, and your thoughts will be established.

How does this verse speak to your soul, heart, and mind?

_____

_____

_____

Daily Gratitude Prayer *(Consider a prayer like the following each morning before you start your day: Lord, thank you for this day. Lord, I am grateful for my health. Lord, thank you for trusting me to serve your people.)*

_____

_____

_____

Spend Time with God *(How did you spend time with God today? Did you pray, read scripture, or share His word with someone?)*

Daily Activity	Time	Daily Activity	Time
	6:00am		1:00pm
	7:00am		2:00pm
	8:00am		3:00pm
	9:00am		4:00pm
	10:00am		5:00pm
	11:00am		6:00pm
	12:00pm		7:00pm

Daily Prayer List *(Before you go to sleep tonight, who in your life requires prayer or what circumstance requires prayer today?)*

1. _____   2. _____

3. _____   4. _____

Prayer Focus: Proverbs 31:30   Date: _____

Charm is deceitful and beauty is passing, but a woman who fears the LORD, she shall be praised.

How does this verse speak to your soul, heart, and mind?

_____

_____

_____

Daily Gratitude Prayer *(Consider a prayer like the following each morning before you start your day: Lord, thank you for this day. Lord, I am grateful for my health. Lord, thank you for trusting me to serve your people.)*

_____

_____

_____

Spend Time with God *(How did you spend time with God today? Did you pray, read scripture, or share His word with someone?)*

Daily Activity	Time	Daily Activity	Time
	6:00am		1:00pm
	7:00am		2:00pm
	8:00am		3:00pm
	9:00am		4:00pm
	10:00am		5:00pm
	11:00am		6:00pm
	12:00pm		7:00pm

Daily Prayer List *(Before you go to sleep tonight, who in your life requires prayer or what circumstance requires prayer today?)*

1. _____   2. _____

3. _____   4. _____

Prayer Focus: Psalm143:10   Date: _____

Teach me to do Your will, For You are my God; Your Spirit is good. Lead me in the land of uprightness.

How does this verse speak to your soul, heart, and mind?

_____

_____

_____

Daily Gratitude Prayer *(Consider a prayer like the following each morning before you start your day: Lord, thank you for this day. Lord, I am grateful for my health. Lord, thank you for trusting me to serve your people.)*

_____

_____

_____

Spend Time with God *(How did you spend time with God today? Did you pray, read scripture, or share His word with someone?)*

Daily Activity	Time	Daily Activity	Time
	6:00am		1:00pm
	7:00am		2:00pm
	8:00am		3:00pm
	9:00am		4:00pm
	10:00am		5:00pm
	11:00am		6:00pm
	12:00pm		7:00pm

Daily Prayer List *(Before you go to sleep tonight, who in your life requires prayer or what circumstance requires prayer today?)*

1. _____   2. _____

3. _____   4. _____

Prayer Focus: Isaiah 41:10   Date: _____

Fear not, for I am with you; Be not dismayed, for I am your God. I will strengthen you, Yes, I will help you, I will uphold you with My righteous right hand.

How does this verse speak to your soul, heart, and mind?

_____

_____

_____

Daily Gratitude Prayer *(Consider a prayer like the following each morning before you start your day: Lord, thank you for this day. Lord, I am grateful for my health. Lord, thank you for trusting me to serve your people.)*

_____

_____

_____

Spend Time with God *(How did you spend time with God today? Did you pray, read scripture, or share His word with someone?)*

Daily Activity	Time	Daily Activity	Time
	6:00am		1:00pm
	7:00am		2:00pm
	8:00am		3:00pm
	9:00am		4:00pm
	10:00am		5:00pm
	11:00am		6:00pm
	12:00pm		7:00pm

Daily Prayer List *(Before you go to sleep tonight, who in your life requires prayer or what circumstance requires prayer today?)*

1. _____   2. _____

3. _____   4. _____

Prayer Focus: Colossians 1:10   Date: _____

That you may walk worthy of the Lord, fully pleasing Him, being fruitful in every good work and increasing in the knowledge of God.

How does this verse speak to your soul, heart, and mind?

_____

_____

_____

Daily Gratitude Prayer *(Consider a prayer like the following each morning before you start your day: Lord, thank you for this day. Lord, I am grateful for my health. Lord, thank you for trusting me to serve your people.)*

_____

_____

_____

Spend Time with God *(How did you spend time with God today? Did you pray, read scripture, or share His word with someone?)*

Daily Activity	Time	Daily Activity	Time
	6:00am		1:00pm
	7:00am		2:00pm
	8:00am		3:00pm
	9:00am		4:00pm
	10:00am		5:00pm
	11:00am		6:00pm
	12:00pm		7:00pm

Daily Prayer List *(Before you go to sleep tonight, who in your life requires prayer or what circumstance requires prayer today?)*

1. _____   2. _____

3. _____   4. _____

Prayer Focus: Psalm 92:4   Date: _____

For You, LORD, have made me glad through Your work; I will triumph in the works of Your hands.

How does this verse speak to your soul, heart, and mind?

_____

_____

_____

Daily Gratitude Prayer *(Consider a prayer like the following each morning before you start your day: Lord, thank you for this day. Lord, I am grateful for my health. Lord, thank you for trusting me to serve your people.)*

_____

_____

_____

Spend Time with God *(How did you spend time with God today? Did you pray, read scripture, or share His word with someone?)*

Daily Activity	Time	Daily Activity	Time
	6:00am		1:00pm
	7:00am		2:00pm
	8:00am		3:00pm
	9:00am		4:00pm
	10:00am		5:00pm
	11:00am		6:00pm
	12:00pm		7:00pm

Daily Prayer List *(Before you go to sleep tonight, who in your life requires prayer or what circumstance requires prayer today?)*

1. _____   2. _____

3. _____   4. _____

Prayer Focus: Mark 9:23   Date: _____

Jesus said to him, "If you can believe, all things are possible to him who believes."

How does this verse speak to your soul, heart, and mind?

_____

_____

_____

Daily Gratitude Prayer *(Consider a prayer like the following each morning before you start your day: Lord, thank you for this day. Lord, I am grateful for my health. Lord, thank you for trusting me to serve your people.)*

_____

_____

_____

Spend Time with God *(How did you spend time with God today? Did you pray, read scripture, or share His word with someone?)*

Daily Activity	Time	Daily Activity	Time
	6:00am		1:00pm
	7:00am		2:00pm
	8:00am		3:00pm
	9:00am		4:00pm
	10:00am		5:00pm
	11:00am		6:00pm
	12:00pm		7:00pm

Daily Prayer List *(Before you go to sleep tonight, who in your life requires prayer or what circumstance requires prayer today?)*

1. _____   2. _____

3. _____   4. _____

Prayer Focus: Proverbs 3:13   Date: _____

Happy is the man who finds wisdom, and the man who gains understanding.

How does this verse speak to your soul, heart, and mind?

_____

_____

_____

Daily Gratitude Prayer *(Consider a prayer like the following each morning before you start your day: Lord, thank you for this day. Lord, I am grateful for my health. Lord, thank you for trusting me to serve your people.)*

_____

_____

_____

Spend Time with God *(How did you spend time with God today? Did you pray, read scripture, or share His word with someone?)*

Daily Activity	Time	Daily Activity	Time
	6:00am		1:00pm
	7:00am		2:00pm
	8:00am		3:00pm
	9:00am		4:00pm
	10:00am		5:00pm
	11:00am		6:00pm
	12:00pm		7:00pm

Daily Prayer List *(Before you go to sleep tonight, who in your life requires prayer or what circumstance requires prayer today?)*

1. _____   2. _____

3. _____   4. _____

Prayer Focus: Galatians 6:9   Date: _____

And let us not grow weary while doing good, for in due season we shall reap if we do not lose heart.

How does this verse speak to your soul, heart, and mind?

_____

_____

_____

Daily Gratitude Prayer *(Consider a prayer like the following each morning before you start your day: Lord, thank you for this day. Lord, I am grateful for my health. Lord, thank you for trusting me to serve your people.)*

_____

_____

_____

Spend Time with God *(How did you spend time with God today? Did you pray, read scripture, or share His word with someone?)*

Daily Activity	Time	Daily Activity	Time
	6:00am		1:00pm
	7:00am		2:00pm
	8:00am		3:00pm
	9:00am		4:00pm
	10:00am		5:00pm
	11:00am		6:00pm
	12:00pm		7:00pm

Daily Prayer List (Before you go to sleep tonight, who in your life requires prayer or what circumstance requires prayer today?)

1. _____

2. _____

3. _____

4. _____

Prayer Focus: John 10:10   Date: _____

The thief does not come except to steal, and to kill, and to destroy. I have come that they may have life, and that they may have it more abundantly.

How does this verse speak to your soul, heart, and mind?

_____

_____

_____

Daily Gratitude Prayer *(Consider a prayer like the following each morning before you start your day: Lord, thank you for this day. Lord, I am grateful for my health. Lord, thank you for trusting me to serve your people.)*

_____

_____

_____

Spend Time with God *(How did you spend time with God today? Did you pray, read scripture, or share His word with someone?)*

Daily Activity	Time	Daily Activity	Time
	6:00am		1:00pm
	7:00am		2:00pm
	8:00am		3:00pm
	9:00am		4:00pm
	10:00am		5:00pm
	11:00am		6:00pm
	12:00pm		7:00pm

Daily Prayer List *(Before you go to sleep tonight, who in your life requires prayer or what circumstance requires prayer today?)*

1. _____   2. _____

3. _____   4. _____

Prayer Focus: Romans 11:29

Date: _____

For the gifts and the calling of God are irrevocable.

How does this verse speak to your soul, heart, and mind?

_____

_____

_____

Daily Gratitude Prayer *(Consider a prayer like the following each morning before you start your day: Lord, thank you for this day. Lord, I am grateful for my health. Lord, thank you for trusting me to serve your people.)*

_____

_____

_____

Spend Time with God *(How did you spend time with God today? Did you pray, read scripture, or share His word with someone?)*

Daily Activity	Time	Daily Activity	Time
	6:00am		1:00pm
	7:00am		2:00pm
	8:00am		3:00pm
	9:00am		4:00pm
	10:00am		5:00pm
	11:00am		6:00pm
	12:00pm		7:00pm

Daily Prayer List *(Before you go to sleep tonight, who in your life requires prayer or what circumstance requires prayer today?)*

1. _____   2. _____

3. _____   4. _____

Prayer Focus: Proverbs 16:20   Date: _____

Whoever gives heed to instruction prospers and blessed is the one who trusts in the LORD.

How does this verse speak to your soul, heart, and mind?

_____

_____

_____

Daily Gratitude Prayer *(Consider a prayer like the following each morning before you start your day: Lord, thank you for this day. Lord, I am grateful for my health. Lord, thank you for trusting me to serve your people.)*

_____

_____

_____

Spend Time with God *(How did you spend time with God today? Did you pray, read scripture, or share His word with someone?)*

Daily Activity	Time	Daily Activity	Time
	6:00am		1:00pm
	7:00am		2:00pm
	8:00am		3:00pm
	9:00am		4:00pm
	10:00am		5:00pm
	11:00am		6:00pm
	12:00pm		7:00pm

Daily Prayer List *(Before you go to sleep tonight, who in your life requires prayer or what circumstance requires prayer today?)*

1. _____   2. _____

3. _____   4. _____

Prayer Focus: Psalm 91:10   Date: _____

No evil shall befall you, nor shall any plague come near your dwelling.

How does this verse speak to your soul, heart, and mind?

_____

_____

_____

Daily Gratitude Prayer *(Consider a prayer like the following each morning before you start your day: Lord, thank you for this day. Lord, I am grateful for my health. Lord, thank you for trusting me to serve your people.)*

_____

_____

_____

Spend Time with God *(How did you spend time with God today? Did you pray, read scripture, or share His word with someone?)*

Daily Activity	Time	Daily Activity	Time
	6:00am		1:00pm
	7:00am		2:00pm
	8:00am		3:00pm
	9:00am		4:00pm
	10:00am		5:00pm
	11:00am		6:00pm
	12:00pm		7:00pm

Daily Prayer List *(Before you go to sleep tonight, who in your life requires prayer or what circumstance requires prayer today?)*

1. _____   2. _____

3. _____   4. _____

Prayer Focus: Deuteronomy 4:29   Date: _____

But from there you will seek the LORD your God, and you will find Him if you seek Him with all your heart and with all your soul.

How does this verse speak to your soul, heart, and mind?

_____

_____

_____

Daily Gratitude Prayer *(Consider a prayer like the following each morning before you start your day: Lord, thank you for this day. Lord, I am grateful for my health. Lord, thank you for trusting me to serve your people.)*

_____

_____

_____

Spend Time with God *(How did you spend time with God today? Did you pray, read scripture, or share His word with someone?)*

Daily Activity	Time	Daily Activity	Time
	6:00am		1:00pm
	7:00am		2:00pm
	8:00am		3:00pm
	9:00am		4:00pm
	10:00am		5:00pm
	11:00am		6:00pm
	12:00pm		7:00pm

Daily Prayer List *(Before you go to sleep tonight, who in your life requires prayer or what circumstance requires prayer today?)*

1. _____ 2. _____

3. _____ 4. _____

Prayer Focus: Luke 1:37

Date: _____

For with God nothing will be impossible.

How does this verse speak to your soul, heart, and mind?

_____

_____

_____

Daily Gratitude Prayer *(Consider a prayer like the following each morning before you start your day: Lord, thank you for this day. Lord, I am grateful for my health. Lord, thank you for trusting me to serve your people.)*

_____

_____

_____

Spend Time with God *(How did you spend time with God today? Did you pray, read scripture, or share His word with someone?)*

Daily Activity	Time	Daily Activity	Time
	6:00am		1:00pm
	7:00am		2:00pm
	8:00am		3:00pm
	9:00am		4:00pm
	10:00am		5:00pm
	11:00am		6:00pm
	12:00pm		7:00pm

Daily Prayer List (Before you go to sleep tonight, who in your life requires prayer or what circumstance requires prayer today?)

1. _____   2. _____

3. _____   4. _____

Prayer Focus: Isaiah 12:2   Date: _____

Surely God is my salvation; I will trust and not be afraid. The LORD, the LORD himself, is my strength and my defense; he has become my salvation.

How does this verse speak to your soul, heart, and mind?

_____

_____

_____

Daily Gratitude Prayer *(Consider a prayer like the following each morning before you start your day: Lord, thank you for this day. Lord, I am grateful for my health. Lord, thank you for trusting me to serve your people.)*

_____

_____

_____

Spend Time with God *(How did you spend time with God today? Did you pray, read scripture, or share His word with someone?)*

Daily Activity	Time	Daily Activity	Time
	6:00am		1:00pm
	7:00am		2:00pm
	8:00am		3:00pm
	9:00am		4:00pm
	10:00am		5:00pm
	11:00am		6:00pm
	12:00pm		7:00pm

Daily Prayer List *(Before you go to sleep tonight, who in your life requires prayer or what circumstance requires prayer today?)*

1. _____   2. _____

3. _____   4. _____

Prayer Focus: 1 John 2:17   Date: _____

The world and its desires pass away, but whoever does the will of God lives forever.

How does this verse speak to your soul, heart, and mind?

_____

_____

_____

Daily Gratitude Prayer *(Consider a prayer like the following each morning before you start your day: Lord, thank you for this day. Lord, I am grateful for my health. Lord, thank you for trusting me to serve your people.)*

_____

_____

_____

Spend Time with God *(How did you spend time with God today? Did you pray, read scripture, or share His word with someone?)*

Daily Activity	Time	Daily Activity	Time
	6:00am		1:00pm
	7:00am		2:00pm
	8:00am		3:00pm
	9:00am		4:00pm
	10:00am		5:00pm
	11:00am		6:00pm
	12:00pm		7:00pm

Daily Prayer List *(Before you go to sleep tonight, who in your life requires prayer or what circumstance requires prayer today?)*

1. _____   2. _____

3. _____   4. _____

Prayer Focus: 2 Corinthians 9:8   Date: _____

A man's heart plans his way, But the LORD directs his steps.

How does this verse speak to your soul, heart, and mind?

_____

_____

_____

Daily Gratitude Prayer *(Consider a prayer like the following each morning before you start your day: Lord, thank you for this day. Lord, I am grateful for my health. Lord, thank you for trusting me to serve your people.)*

_____

_____

_____

Spend Time with God *(How did you spend time with God today? Did you pray, read scripture, or share His word with someone?)*

Daily Activity	Time	Daily Activity	Time
	6:00am		1:00pm
	7:00am		2:00pm
	8:00am		3:00pm
	9:00am		4:00pm
	10:00am		5:00pm
	11:00am		6:00pm
	12:00pm		7:00pm

Daily Prayer List *(Before you go to sleep tonight, who in your life requires prayer or what circumstance requires prayer today?)*

1. _____   2. _____

3. _____   4. _____

Prayer Focus: Romans 8:11   Date: _____

But if the Spirit of Him who raised Jesus from the dead dwells in you, He who raised Christ from the dead will also give life to your mortal bodies through His Spirit who dwells in you.

How does this verse speak to your soul, heart, and mind?

_____

_____

_____

Daily Gratitude Prayer *(Consider a prayer like the following each morning before you start your day: Lord, thank you for this day. Lord, I am grateful for my health. Lord, thank you for trusting me to serve your people.)*

_____

_____

_____

Spend Time with God *(How did you spend time with God today? Did you pray, read scripture, or share His word with someone?)*

Daily Activity	Time	Daily Activity	Time
	6:00am		1:00pm
	7:00am		2:00pm
	8:00am		3:00pm
	9:00am		4:00pm
	10:00am		5:00pm
	11:00am		6:00pm
	12:00pm		7:00pm

Daily Prayer List *(Before you go to sleep tonight, who in your life requires prayer or what circumstance requires prayer today?)*

1. _____   2. _____

3. _____   4. _____

Prayer Focus: Job 23:10   Date: _____

But he knows the way that I take; when he has tested me, I will come forth as gold.

How does this verse speak to your soul, heart, and mind?

_____

_____

_____

Daily Gratitude Prayer *(Consider a prayer like the following each morning before you start your day: Lord, thank you for this day. Lord, I am grateful for my health. Lord, thank you for trusting me to serve your people.)*

_____

_____

_____

Spend Time with God *(How did you spend time with God today? Did you pray, read scripture, or share His word with someone?)*

Daily Activity	Time	Daily Activity	Time
	6:00am		1:00pm
	7:00am		2:00pm
	8:00am		3:00pm
	9:00am		4:00pm
	10:00am		5:00pm
	11:00am		6:00pm
	12:00pm		7:00pm

Daily Prayer List *(Before you go to sleep tonight, who in your life requires prayer or what circumstance requires prayer today?)*

1. _____   2. _____

3. _____   4. _____

Prayer Focus: Philippians 4:5

Date: _____

Let your gentleness be evident to all. The Lord is near.

How does this verse speak to your soul, heart, and mind?

_____

_____

_____

Daily Gratitude Prayer *(Consider a prayer like the following each morning before you start your day: Lord, thank you for this day. Lord, I am grateful for my health. Lord, thank you for trusting me to serve your people.)*

_____

_____

_____

Spend Time with God *(How did you spend time with God today? Did you pray, read scripture, or share His word with someone?)*

Daily Activity	Time	Daily Activity	Time
	6:00am		1:00pm
	7:00am		2:00pm
	8:00am		3:00pm
	9:00am		4:00pm
	10:00am		5:00pm
	11:00am		6:00pm
	12:00pm		7:00pm

Daily Prayer List (Before you go to sleep tonight, who in your life requires prayer or what circumstance requires prayer today?)

1. _____

2. _____

3. _____

4. _____

Prayer Focus: Hebrews 10:35   Date: _____

Therefore, do not cast away your confidence, which has great reward.

How does this verse speak to your soul, heart, and mind?

_____

_____

_____

Daily Gratitude Prayer *(Consider a prayer like the following each morning before you start your day: Lord, thank you for this day. Lord, I am grateful for my health. Lord, thank you for trusting me to serve your people.)*

_____

_____

_____

Spend Time with God *(How did you spend time with God today? Did you pray, read scripture, or share His word with someone?)*

Daily Activity	Time	Daily Activity	Time
	6:00am		1:00pm
	7:00am		2:00pm
	8:00am		3:00pm
	9:00am		4:00pm
	10:00am		5:00pm
	11:00am		6:00pm
	12:00pm		7:00pm

Daily Prayer List *(Before you go to sleep tonight, who in your life requires prayer or what circumstance requires prayer today?)*

1. _____   2. _____

3. _____   4. _____

Prayer Focus: Matthew 21:22   Date: _____

And whatever things you ask in prayer, believing, you will receive.

How does this verse speak to your soul, heart, and mind?

_____

_____

_____

Daily Gratitude Prayer *(Consider a prayer like the following each morning before you start your day: Lord, thank you for this day. Lord, I am grateful for my health. Lord, thank you for trusting me to serve your people.)*

_____

_____

_____

Spend Time with God *(How did you spend time with God today? Did you pray, read scripture, or share His word with someone?)*

Daily Activity	Time	Daily Activity	Time
	6:00am		1:00pm
	7:00am		2:00pm
	8:00am		3:00pm
	9:00am		4:00pm
	10:00am		5:00pm
	11:00am		6:00pm
	12:00pm		7:00pm

Daily Prayer List *(Before you go to sleep tonight, who in your life requires prayer or what circumstance requires prayer today?)*

1. _____   2. _____

3. _____   4. _____

Prayer Focus: Psalm 32:8   Date: _____

I will instruct you and teach you in the way you should go; I will guide you with My eye.

How does this verse speak to your soul, heart, and mind?

_____

_____

_____

Daily Gratitude Prayer *(Consider a prayer like the following each morning before you start your day: Lord, thank you for this day. Lord, I am grateful for my health. Lord, thank you for trusting me to serve your people.)*

_____

_____

_____

Spend Time with God *(How did you spend time with God today? Did you pray, read scripture, or share His word with someone?)*

Daily Activity	Time	Daily Activity	Time
	6:00am		1:00pm
	7:00am		2:00pm
	8:00am		3:00pm
	9:00am		4:00pm
	10:00am		5:00pm
	11:00am		6:00pm
	12:00pm		7:00pm

Daily Prayer List *(Before you go to sleep tonight, who in your life requires prayer or what circumstance requires prayer today?)*

1. _____   2. _____

3. _____   4. _____

Prayer Focus: Proverbs 22:4   Date: _____

The reward of humility and the fear of the LORD Are riches, honor, and life.

How does this verse speak to your soul, heart, and mind?

_____

_____

_____

Daily Gratitude Prayer *(Consider a prayer like the following each morning before you start your day: Lord, thank you for this day. Lord, I am grateful for my health. Lord, thank you for trusting me to serve your people.)*

_____

_____

_____

Spend Time with God *(How did you spend time with God today? Did you pray, read scripture, or share His word with someone?)*

Daily Activity	Time	Daily Activity	Time
	6:00am		1:00pm
	7:00am		2:00pm
	8:00am		3:00pm
	9:00am		4:00pm
	10:00am		5:00pm
	11:00am		6:00pm
	12:00pm		7:00pm

Daily Prayer List *(Before you go to sleep tonight, who in your life requires prayer or what circumstance requires prayer today?)*

1. _____   2. _____

3. _____   4. _____

Prayer Focus: Isaiah 55:11   Date: _____

So shall My word be that goes forth from My mouth; It shall not return to Me void, but it shall accomplish what I please, and it shall prosper in the thing for which I sent it.

How does this verse speak to your soul, heart, and mind?

_____

_____

_____

Daily Gratitude Prayer *(Consider a prayer like the following each morning before you start your day: Lord, thank you for this day. Lord, I am grateful for my health. Lord, thank you for trusting me to serve your people.)*

_____

_____

_____

Spend Time with God *(How did you spend time with God today? Did you pray, read scripture, or share His word with someone?)*

Daily Activity	Time	Daily Activity	Time
	6:00am		1:00pm
	7:00am		2:00pm
	8:00am		3:00pm
	9:00am		4:00pm
	10:00am		5:00pm
	11:00am		6:00pm
	12:00pm		7:00pm

Daily Prayer List *(Before you go to sleep tonight, who in your life requires prayer or what circumstance requires prayer today?)*

1. _____   2. _____

3. _____   4. _____

Prayer Focus: Proverbs 19:21

Date: _____

Many are the plans in a person's heart, but it is the LORD's purpose that prevails.

How does this verse speak to your soul, heart, and mind?

_____

_____

_____

Daily Gratitude Prayer *(Consider a prayer like the following each morning before you start your day: Lord, thank you for this day. Lord, I am grateful for my health. Lord, thank you for trusting me to serve your people.)*

_____

_____

_____

Spend Time with God *(How did you spend time with God today? Did you pray, read scripture, or share His word with someone?)*

Daily Activity	Time	Daily Activity	Time
	6:00am		1:00pm
	7:00am		2:00pm
	8:00am		3:00pm
	9:00am		4:00pm
	10:00am		5:00pm
	11:00am		6:00pm
	12:00pm		7:00pm

Daily Prayer List *(Before you go to sleep tonight, who in your life requires prayer or what circumstance requires prayer today?)*

1. _____   2. _____

3. _____   4. _____

Prayer Focus: Colossians 3:10   Date: _____

and have put on the new self, which is being renewed in knowledge in the image of its Creator.

How does this verse speak to your soul, heart, and mind?

_____

_____

_____

Daily Gratitude Prayer *(Consider a prayer like the following each morning before you start your day: Lord, thank you for this day. Lord, I am grateful for my health. Lord, thank you for trusting me to serve your people.)*

_____

_____

_____

Spend Time with God *(How did you spend time with God today? Did you pray, read scripture, or share His word with someone?)*

Daily Activity	Time	Daily Activity	Time
	6:00am		1:00pm
	7:00am		2:00pm
	8:00am		3:00pm
	9:00am		4:00pm
	10:00am		5:00pm
	11:00am		6:00pm
	12:00pm		7:00pm

Daily Prayer List *(Before you go to sleep tonight, who in your life requires prayer or what circumstance requires prayer today?)*

1. _____   2. _____

3. _____   4. _____

Prayer Focus: Proverbs 16:3   Date: _____

Commit to the LORD whatever you do, and he will establish your plans.

How does this verse speak to your soul, heart, and mind?

_____

_____

_____

Daily Gratitude Prayer *(Consider a prayer like the following each morning before you start your day: Lord, thank you for this day. Lord, I am grateful for my health. Lord, thank you for trusting me to serve your people.)*

_____

_____

_____

Spend Time with God *(How did you spend time with God today? Did you pray, read scripture, or share His word with someone?)*

Daily Activity	Time	Daily Activity	Time
	6:00am		1:00pm
	7:00am		2:00pm
	8:00am		3:00pm
	9:00am		4:00pm
	10:00am		5:00pm
	11:00am		6:00pm
	12:00pm		7:00pm

Daily Prayer List *(Before you go to sleep tonight, who in your life requires prayer or what circumstance requires prayer today?)*

1. _____   2. _____

3. _____   4. _____

Prayer Focus: 2 Timothy 3:17   Date: _____

So that the man or woman of God may be fully capable, equipped for every good work.

How does this verse speak to your soul, heart, and mind?

_____

_____

_____

Daily Gratitude Prayer *(Consider a prayer like the following each morning before you start your day: Lord, thank you for this day. Lord, I am grateful for my health. Lord, thank you for trusting me to serve your people.)*

_____

_____

_____

Spend Time with God *(How did you spend time with God today? Did you pray, read scripture, or share His word with someone?)*

Daily Activity	Time	Daily Activity	Time
	6:00am		1:00pm
	7:00am		2:00pm
	8:00am		3:00pm
	9:00am		4:00pm
	10:00am		5:00pm
	11:00am		6:00pm
	12:00pm		7:00pm

Daily Prayer List *(Before you go to sleep tonight, who in your life requires prayer or what circumstance requires prayer today?)*

1. _____   2. _____

3. _____   4. _____

Prayer Focus: 1 Thessalonians 4:7   Date: _____

For God has not called us for impurity, but in sanctification.

How does this verse speak to your soul, heart, and mind?

_____

_____

_____

Daily Gratitude Prayer *(Consider a prayer like the following each morning before you start your day: Lord, thank you for this day. Lord, I am grateful for my health. Lord, thank you for trusting me to serve your people.)*

_____

_____

_____

Spend Time with God *(How did you spend time with God today? Did you pray, read scripture, or share His word with someone?)*

Daily Activity	Time	Daily Activity	Time
	6:00am		1:00pm
	7:00am		2:00pm
	8:00am		3:00pm
	9:00am		4:00pm
	10:00am		5:00pm
	11:00am		6:00pm
	12:00pm		7:00pm

Daily Prayer List *(Before you go to sleep tonight, who in your life requires prayer or what circumstance requires prayer today?)*

1. _____   2. _____

3. _____   4. _____

Prayer Focus: Psalm 139:14   Date: _____

I will praise You, for I am fearfully and wonderfully made; Marvelous are Your works, and that my soul knows very well.

How does this verse speak to your soul, heart, and mind?

_____

_____

_____

Daily Gratitude Prayer *(Consider a prayer like the following each morning before you start your day: Lord, thank you for this day. Lord, I am grateful for my health. Lord, thank you for trusting me to serve your people.)*

_____

_____

_____

Spend Time with God *(How did you spend time with God today? Did you pray, read scripture, or share His word with someone?)*

Daily Activity	Time	Daily Activity	Time
	6:00am		1:00pm
	7:00am		2:00pm
	8:00am		3:00pm
	9:00am		4:00pm
	10:00am		5:00pm
	11:00am		6:00pm
	12:00pm		7:00pm

Daily Prayer List (Before you go to sleep tonight, who in your life requires prayer or what circumstance requires prayer today?)

1. _____   2. _____

3. _____   4. _____

Prayer Focus: James 1:22   Date: _____

But be doers of the word, and not hearers only, deceiving yourselves.

How does this verse speak to your soul, heart, and mind?

_____

_____

_____

Daily Gratitude Prayer *(Consider a prayer like the following each morning before you start your day: Lord, thank you for this day. Lord, I am grateful for my health. Lord, thank you for trusting me to serve your people.)*

_____

_____

_____

Spend Time with God *(How did you spend time with God today? Did you pray, read scripture, or share His word with someone?)*

Daily Activity	Time	Daily Activity	Time
	6:00am		1:00pm
	7:00am		2:00pm
	8:00am		3:00pm
	9:00am		4:00pm
	10:00am		5:00pm
	11:00am		6:00pm
	12:00pm		7:00pm

Daily Prayer List *(Before you go to sleep tonight, who in your life requires prayer or what circumstance requires prayer today?)*

1. _____   2. _____

3. _____   4. _____

Prayer Focus: Hebrews 6:1   Date: _____

Therefore, let us move beyond the elementary teachings about Christ and be taken forward to maturity, not laying again the foundation of repentance from acts that lead to death, and of faith in God.

How does this verse speak to your soul, heart, and mind?

_____

_____

_____

Daily Gratitude Prayer *(Consider a prayer like the following each morning before you start your day: Lord, thank you for this day. Lord, I am grateful for my health. Lord, thank you for trusting me to serve your people.)*

_____

_____

_____

Spend Time with God *(How did you spend time with God today? Did you pray, read scripture, or share His word with someone?)*

Daily Activity	Time	Daily Activity	Time
	6:00am		1:00pm
	7:00am		2:00pm
	8:00am		3:00pm
	9:00am		4:00pm
	10:00am		5:00pm
	11:00am		6:00pm
	12:00pm		7:00pm

Daily Prayer List *(Before you go to sleep tonight, who in your life requires prayer or what circumstance requires prayer today?)*

1. _____   2. _____

3. _____   4. _____

Prayer Focus: Psalm 34:4   Date: _____

I sought the LORD, and he answered me; he delivered me from all my fears.

How does this verse speak to your soul, heart, and mind?

_____

_____

_____

Daily Gratitude Prayer *(Consider a prayer like the following each morning before you start your day: Lord, thank you for this day. Lord, I am grateful for my health. Lord, thank you for trusting me to serve your people.)*

_____

_____

_____

Spend Time with God *(How did you spend time with God today? Did you pray, read scripture, or share His word with someone?)*

Daily Activity	Time	Daily Activity	Time
	6:00am		1:00pm
	7:00am		2:00pm
	8:00am		3:00pm
	9:00am		4:00pm
	10:00am		5:00pm
	11:00am		6:00pm
	12:00pm		7:00pm

Daily Prayer List *(Before you go to sleep tonight, who in your life requires prayer or what circumstance requires prayer today?)*

1. _____   2. _____

3. _____   4. _____

Prayer Focus: Psalm 141:3   Date: _____

Set a guard over my mouth, LORD; keep watch over the door of my lips.

How does this verse speak to your soul, heart, and mind?

_____

_____

_____

Daily Gratitude Prayer *(Consider a prayer like the following each morning before you start your day: Lord, thank you for this day. Lord, I am grateful for my health. Lord, thank you for trusting me to serve your people.)*

_____

_____

_____

Spend Time with God *(How did you spend time with God today? Did you pray, read scripture, or share His word with someone?)*

Daily Activity	Time	Daily Activity	Time
	6:00am		1:00pm
	7:00am		2:00pm
	8:00am		3:00pm
	9:00am		4:00pm
	10:00am		5:00pm
	11:00am		6:00pm
	12:00pm		7:00pm

Daily Prayer List *(Before you go to sleep tonight, who in your life requires prayer or what circumstance requires prayer today?)*

1. _____   2. _____

3. _____   4. _____

Prayer Focus: 1 Corinthians 9:26-27   Date: _____

Therefore, I run in such a way as not to run aimlessly; I box in such a way, as to avoid hitting air; but I strictly discipline my body and make it my slave, so that, after I have preached to others, I myself will not be disqualified.

How does this verse speak to your soul, heart, and mind?

_____

_____

_____

Daily Gratitude Prayer *(Consider a prayer like the following each morning before you start your day: Lord, thank you for this day. Lord, I am grateful for my health. Lord, thank you for trusting me to serve your people.)*

_____

_____

_____

Spend Time with God *(How did you spend time with God today? Did you pray, read scripture, or share His word with someone?)*

Daily Activity	Time	Daily Activity	Time
	6:00am		1:00pm
	7:00am		2:00pm
	8:00am		3:00pm
	9:00am		4:00pm
	10:00am		5:00pm
	11:00am		6:00pm
	12:00pm		7:00pm

Daily Prayer List *(Before you go to sleep tonight, who in your life requires prayer or what circumstance requires prayer today?)*

1. _____   2. _____

3. _____   4. _____

Prayer Focus: John 42:2   Date: _____

I know that You can do everything, and that no purpose of Yours can be withheld from You.

How does this verse speak to your soul, heart, and mind?

_____

_____

_____

Daily Gratitude Prayer *(Consider a prayer like the following each morning before you start your day: Lord, thank you for this day. Lord, I am grateful for my health. Lord, thank you for trusting me to serve your people.)*

_____

_____

_____

Spend Time with God *(How did you spend time with God today? Did you pray, read scripture, or share His word with someone?)*

Daily Activity	Time	Daily Activity	Time
	6:00am		1:00pm
	7:00am		2:00pm
	8:00am		3:00pm
	9:00am		4:00pm
	10:00am		5:00pm
	11:00am		6:00pm
	12:00pm		7:00pm

Daily Prayer List *(Before you go to sleep tonight, who in your life requires prayer or what circumstance requires prayer today?)*

1. _____   2. _____

3. _____   4. _____

Prayer Focus: 1 Corinthians 16:13   Date: _____

Be on your guard; stand firm in the faith; be courageous; be strong.

How does this verse speak to your soul, heart, and mind?

_____

_____

_____

Daily Gratitude Prayer *(Consider a prayer like the following each morning before you start your day: Lord, thank you for this day. Lord, I am grateful for my health. Lord, thank you for trusting me to serve your people.)*

_____

_____

_____

Spend Time with God *(How did you spend time with God today? Did you pray, read scripture, or share His word with someone?)*

Daily Activity	Time	Daily Activity	Time
	6:00am		1:00pm
	7:00am		2:00pm
	8:00am		3:00pm
	9:00am		4:00pm
	10:00am		5:00pm
	11:00am		6:00pm
	12:00pm		7:00pm

Daily Prayer List (Before you go to sleep tonight, who in your life requires prayer or what circumstance requires prayer today?)

1. _____   2. _____

3. _____   4. _____

Prayer Focus: Isaiah 26:3   Date: _____

You will keep in perfect peace those whose minds are steadfast because they trust in you.

How does this verse speak to your soul, heart, and mind?

_____

_____

_____

Daily Gratitude Prayer *(Consider a prayer like the following each morning before you start your day: Lord, thank you for this day. Lord, I am grateful for my health. Lord, thank you for trusting me to serve your people.)*

_____

_____

_____

Spend Time with God *(How did you spend time with God today? Did you pray, read scripture, or share His word with someone?)*

Daily Activity	Time	Daily Activity	Time
	6:00am		1:00pm
	7:00am		2:00pm
	8:00am		3:00pm
	9:00am		4:00pm
	10:00am		5:00pm
	11:00am		6:00pm
	12:00pm		7:00pm

Daily Prayer List *(Before you go to sleep tonight, who in your life requires prayer or what circumstance requires prayer today?)*

1. _____   2. _____

3. _____   4. _____

Prayer Focus: Ecclesiastes 3:1   Date: _____

There is a time for everything, and a season for every activity under the heavens.

How does this verse speak to your soul, heart, and mind?

_____

_____

_____

Daily Gratitude Prayer *(Consider a prayer like the following each morning before you start your day: Lord, thank you for this day. Lord, I am grateful for my health. Lord, thank you for trusting me to serve your people.)*

_____

_____

_____

Spend Time with God *(How did you spend time with God today? Did you pray, read scripture, or share His word with someone?)*

Daily Activity	Time	Daily Activity	Time
	6:00am		1:00pm
	7:00am		2:00pm
	8:00am		3:00pm
	9:00am		4:00pm
	10:00am		5:00pm
	11:00am		6:00pm
	12:00pm		7:00pm

Daily Prayer List *(Before you go to sleep tonight, who in your life requires prayer or what circumstance requires prayer today?)*

1. _____   2. _____

3. _____   4. _____

Prayer Focus: Matthew 5:37　　　　Date: _____

All you need to say is simply 'Yes' or 'No' anything beyond this comes from the evil one.

How does this verse speak to your soul, heart, and mind?

_____

_____

_____

Daily Gratitude Prayer *(Consider a prayer like the following each morning before you start your day: Lord, thank you for this day. Lord, I am grateful for my health. Lord, thank you for trusting me to serve your people.)*

_____

_____

_____

Spend Time with God *(How did you spend time with God today? Did you pray, read scripture, or share His word with someone?)*

Daily Activity	Time	Daily Activity	Time
	6:00am		1:00pm
	7:00am		2:00pm
	8:00am		3:00pm
	9:00am		4:00pm
	10:00am		5:00pm
	11:00am		6:00pm
	12:00pm		7:00pm

Daily Prayer List *(Before you go to sleep tonight, who in your life requires prayer or what circumstance requires prayer today?)*

1. _____　　2. _____

3. _____　　4. _____

Prayer Focus: Proverbs 20:7　　　　Date: _____

The righteous lead blameless lives; blessed are their children after them.

How does this verse speak to your soul, heart, and mind?

_____

_____

_____

Daily Gratitude Prayer *(Consider a prayer like the following each morning before you start your day: Lord, thank you for this day. Lord, I am grateful for my health. Lord, thank you for trusting me to serve your people.)*

_____

_____

_____

Spend Time with God *(How did you spend time with God today? Did you pray, read scripture, or share His word with someone?)*

Daily Activity	Time	Daily Activity	Time
	6:00am		1:00pm
	7:00am		2:00pm
	8:00am		3:00pm
	9:00am		4:00pm
	10:00am		5:00pm
	11:00am		6:00pm
	12:00pm		7:00pm

Daily Prayer List *(Before you go to sleep tonight, who in your life requires prayer or what circumstance requires prayer today?)*

1. _____　　2. _____

3. _____　　4. _____

Prayer Focus: Romans 8:37   Date: _____

Yet in all these things we are more than conquerors through Him who loved us.

How does this verse speak to your soul, heart, and mind?

_____

_____

_____

Daily Gratitude Prayer *(Consider a prayer like the following each morning before you start your day: Lord, thank you for this day. Lord, I am grateful for my health. Lord, thank you for trusting me to serve your people.)*

_____

_____

_____

Spend Time with God *(How did you spend time with God today? Did you pray, read scripture, or share His word with someone?)*

Daily Activity	Time	Daily Activity	Time
	6:00am		1:00pm
	7:00am		2:00pm
	8:00am		3:00pm
	9:00am		4:00pm
	10:00am		5:00pm
	11:00am		6:00pm
	12:00pm		7:00pm

Daily Prayer List (Before you go to sleep tonight, who in your life requires prayer or what circumstance requires prayer today?)

1. _____   2. _____

3. _____   4. _____

Prayer Focus: Luke 8:15   Date: _____

But the ones that fell on the good ground are those who, having heard the word with a noble and good heart, keep it and bear fruit with patience.

How does this verse speak to your soul, heart, and mind?

_____

_____

_____

Daily Gratitude Prayer *(Consider a prayer like the following each morning before you start your day: Lord, thank you for this day. Lord, I am grateful for my health. Lord, thank you for trusting me to serve your people.)*

_____

_____

_____

Spend Time with God *(How did you spend time with God today? Did you pray, read scripture, or share His word with someone?)*

Daily Activity	Time	Daily Activity	Time
	6:00am		1:00pm
	7:00am		2:00pm
	8:00am		3:00pm
	9:00am		4:00pm
	10:00am		5:00pm
	11:00am		6:00pm
	12:00pm		7:00pm

Daily Prayer List *(Before you go to sleep tonight, who in your life requires prayer or what circumstance requires prayer today?)*

1. _____   2. _____

3. _____   4. _____

Prayer Focus: 1 John 3:2   Date: _____

Beloved, now we are children of God; and it has not yet been revealed what we shall be, but we know that when He is revealed, we shall be like Him, for we shall see Him as He is.

How does this verse speak to your soul, heart, and mind?

_____

_____

_____

Daily Gratitude Prayer *(Consider a prayer like the following each morning before you start your day: Lord, thank you for this day. Lord, I am grateful for my health. Lord, thank you for trusting me to serve your people.)*

_____

_____

_____

Spend Time with God *(How did you spend time with God today? Did you pray, read scripture, or share His word with someone?)*

Daily Activity	Time	Daily Activity	Time
	6:00am		1:00pm
	7:00am		2:00pm
	8:00am		3:00pm
	9:00am		4:00pm
	10:00am		5:00pm
	11:00am		6:00pm
	12:00pm		7:00pm

Daily Prayer List *(Before you go to sleep tonight, who in your life requires prayer or what circumstance requires prayer today?)*

1. _____   2. _____

3. _____   4. _____

Prayer Focus: Mark 11:23   Date: _____

For assuredly, I say to you, whoever says to this mountain, 'Be removed and be cast into the sea,' and does not doubt in his heart, but believes that those things he says will be done, he will have whatever he says.

How does this verse speak to your soul, heart, and mind?

_____

_____

_____

Daily Gratitude Prayer *(Consider a prayer like the following each morning before you start your day: Lord, thank you for this day. Lord, I am grateful for my health. Lord, thank you for trusting me to serve your people.)*

_____

_____

_____

Spend Time with God *(How did you spend time with God today? Did you pray, read scripture, or share His word with someone?)*

Daily Activity	Time	Daily Activity	Time
	6:00am		1:00pm
	7:00am		2:00pm
	8:00am		3:00pm
	9:00am		4:00pm
	10:00am		5:00pm
	11:00am		6:00pm
	12:00pm		7:00pm

Daily Prayer List *(Before you go to sleep tonight, who in your life requires prayer or what circumstance requires prayer today?)*

1. _____   2. _____

3. _____   4. _____

Prayer Focus: Matthew 5:16   Date: _____

Let your light so shine before men, that they may see your good works and glorify your Father in heaven.

How does this verse speak to your soul, heart, and mind?

_____

_____

_____

Daily Gratitude Prayer *(Consider a prayer like the following each morning before you start your day: Lord, thank you for this day. Lord, I am grateful for my health. Lord, thank you for trusting me to serve your people.)*

_____

_____

_____

Spend Time with God *(How did you spend time with God today? Did you pray, read scripture, or share His word with someone?)*

Daily Activity	Time	Daily Activity	Time
	6:00am		1:00pm
	7:00am		2:00pm
	8:00am		3:00pm
	9:00am		4:00pm
	10:00am		5:00pm
	11:00am		6:00pm
	12:00pm		7:00pm

Daily Prayer List *(Before you go to sleep tonight, who in your life requires prayer or what circumstance requires prayer today?)*

1. _____   2. _____

3. _____   4. _____

Prayer Focus: 1 Thessalonians 5:16-18   Date: _____

Rejoice always, pray without ceasing, in everything give thanks; for this is the will of God in Christ Jesus for you.

How does this verse speak to your soul, heart, and mind?

_____

_____

_____

Daily Gratitude Prayer *(Consider a prayer like the following each morning before you start your day: Lord, thank you for this day. Lord, I am grateful for my health. Lord, thank you for trusting me to serve your people.)*

_____

_____

_____

Spend Time with God *(How did you spend time with God today? Did you pray, read scripture, or share His word with someone?)*

Daily Activity	Time	Daily Activity	Time
	6:00am		1:00pm
	7:00am		2:00pm
	8:00am		3:00pm
	9:00am		4:00pm
	10:00am		5:00pm
	11:00am		6:00pm
	12:00pm		7:00pm

Daily Prayer List *(Before you go to sleep tonight, who in your life requires prayer or what circumstance requires prayer today?)*

1. _____   2. _____

3. _____   4. _____

Prayer Focus: Luke 15:32   Date: _____

It was right that we should make merry and be glad, for your brother was dead and is alive again, and was lost and is found.

How does this verse speak to your soul, heart, and mind?

_____

_____

_____

Daily Gratitude Prayer *(Consider a prayer like the following each morning before you start your day: Lord, thank you for this day. Lord, I am grateful for my health. Lord, thank you for trusting me to serve your people.)*

_____

_____

_____

Spend Time with God *(How did you spend time with God today? Did you pray, read scripture, or share His word with someone?)*

Daily Activity	Time	Daily Activity	Time
	6:00am		1:00pm
	7:00am		2:00pm
	8:00am		3:00pm
	9:00am		4:00pm
	10:00am		5:00pm
	11:00am		6:00pm
	12:00pm		7:00pm

Daily Prayer List *(Before you go to sleep tonight, who in your life requires prayer or what circumstance requires prayer today?)*

1. _____   2. _____

3. _____   4. _____

Prayer Focus: 2 Samuel 23:12   Date: _____

But he stationed himself in the middle of the field, defended it, and killed the Philistines. So, the LORD brought about a great victory.

How does this verse speak to your soul, heart, and mind?

_____

_____

_____

Daily Gratitude Prayer *(Consider a prayer like the following each morning before you start your day: Lord, thank you for this day. Lord, I am grateful for my health. Lord, thank you for trusting me to serve your people.)*

_____

_____

_____

Spend Time with God *(How did you spend time with God today? Did you pray, read scripture, or share His word with someone?)*

Daily Activity	Time	Daily Activity	Time
	6:00am		1:00pm
	7:00am		2:00pm
	8:00am		3:00pm
	9:00am		4:00pm
	10:00am		5:00pm
	11:00am		6:00pm
	12:00pm		7:00pm

Daily Prayer List (Before you go to sleep tonight, who in your life requires prayer or what circumstance requires prayer today?)

1. _____   2. _____

3. _____   4. _____

Prayer Focus: 1 Timothy 4:10   Date: _____

For to this end, we both labor and suffer reproach, because we trust in the living God, who is the Savior of all men, especially of those who believe.

How does this verse speak to your soul, heart, and mind?

_____

_____

_____

Daily Gratitude Prayer *(Consider a prayer like the following each morning before you start your day: Lord, thank you for this day. Lord, I am grateful for my health. Lord, thank you for trusting me to serve your people.)*

_____

_____

_____

Spend Time with God *(How did you spend time with God today? Did you pray, read scripture, or share His word with someone?)*

Daily Activity	Time	Daily Activity	Time
	6:00am		1:00pm
	7:00am		2:00pm
	8:00am		3:00pm
	9:00am		4:00pm
	10:00am		5:00pm
	11:00am		6:00pm
	12:00pm		7:00pm

Daily Prayer List *(Before you go to sleep tonight, who in your life requires prayer or what circumstance requires prayer today?)*

1. _____   2. _____

3. _____   4. _____

Prayer Focus: Titus 1:8

Date: _____

Rather, he must be hospitable, one who loves what is good, who is self-controlled, upright, holy and disciplined.

How does this verse speak to your soul, heart, and mind?

_____

_____

_____

Daily Gratitude Prayer *(Consider a prayer like the following each morning before you start your day: Lord, thank you for this day. Lord, I am grateful for my health. Lord, thank you for trusting me to serve your people.)*

_____

_____

_____

Spend Time with God *(How did you spend time with God today? Did you pray, read scripture, or share His word with someone?)*

Daily Activity	Time	Daily Activity	Time
	6:00am		1:00pm
	7:00am		2:00pm
	8:00am		3:00pm
	9:00am		4:00pm
	10:00am		5:00pm
	11:00am		6:00pm
	12:00pm		7:00pm

Daily Prayer List *(Before you go to sleep tonight, who in your life requires prayer or what circumstance requires prayer today?)*

1. _____

2. _____

3. _____

4. _____

Prayer Focus: Ephesians 6:10

Date: _____

Finally, be strong in the Lord and in his mighty power.

How does this verse speak to your soul, heart, and mind?

_____

_____

_____

Daily Gratitude Prayer *(Consider a prayer like the following each morning before you start your day: Lord, thank you for this day. Lord, I am grateful for my health. Lord, thank you for trusting me to serve your people.)*

_____

_____

_____

Spend Time with God *(How did you spend time with God today? Did you pray, read scripture, or share His word with someone?)*

Daily Activity	Time	Daily Activity	Time
	6:00am		1:00pm
	7:00am		2:00pm
	8:00am		3:00pm
	9:00am		4:00pm
	10:00am		5:00pm
	11:00am		6:00pm
	12:00pm		7:00pm

Daily Prayer List *(Before you go to sleep tonight, who in your life requires prayer or what circumstance requires prayer today?)*

1. _____

2. _____

3. _____

4. _____

Prayer Focus: Proverbs 4:13

Date: _____

Take firm hold of instruction, do not let go; Keep her, for she is your life.

How does this verse speak to your soul, heart, and mind?

_____

_____

_____

Daily Gratitude Prayer *(Consider a prayer like the following each morning before you start your day: Lord, thank you for this day. Lord, I am grateful for my health. Lord, thank you for trusting me to serve your people.)*

_____

_____

_____

Spend Time with God *(How did you spend time with God today? Did you pray, read scripture, or share His word with someone?)*

Daily Activity	Time	Daily Activity	Time
	6:00am		1:00pm
	7:00am		2:00pm
	8:00am		3:00pm
	9:00am		4:00pm
	10:00am		5:00pm
	11:00am		6:00pm
	12:00pm		7:00pm

Daily Prayer List (Before you go to sleep tonight, who in your life requires prayer or what circumstance requires prayer today?)

1. _____   2. _____

3. _____   4. _____

Prayer Focus: 2 John 1:8   Date: _____

Look to yourselves, that we do not lose those things we worked for, but that we may receive a full reward.

How does this verse speak to your soul, heart, and mind?

_____

_____

_____

Daily Gratitude Prayer *(Consider a prayer like the following each morning before you start your day: Lord, thank you for this day. Lord, I am grateful for my health. Lord, thank you for trusting me to serve your people.)*

_____

_____

_____

Spend Time with God *(How did you spend time with God today? Did you pray, read scripture, or share His word with someone?)*

Daily Activity	Time	Daily Activity	Time
	6:00am		1:00pm
	7:00am		2:00pm
	8:00am		3:00pm
	9:00am		4:00pm
	10:00am		5:00pm
	11:00am		6:00pm
	12:00pm		7:00pm

Daily Prayer List *(Before you go to sleep tonight, who in your life requires prayer or what circumstance requires prayer today?)*

1. _____   2. _____

3. _____   4. _____

Prayer Focus: Isaiah 60:1   Date: _____

Arise, shine; For your light has come! And the glory of the LORD is risen upon you.

How does this verse speak to your soul, heart, and mind?

_____

_____

_____

Daily Gratitude Prayer *(Consider a prayer like the following each morning before you start your day: Lord, thank you for this day. Lord, I am grateful for my health. Lord, thank you for trusting me to serve your people.)*

_____

_____

_____

Spend Time with God *(How did you spend time with God today? Did you pray, read scripture, or share His word with someone?)*

Daily Activity	Time	Daily Activity	Time
	6:00am		1:00pm
	7:00am		2:00pm
	8:00am		3:00pm
	9:00am		4:00pm
	10:00am		5:00pm
	11:00am		6:00pm
	12:00pm		7:00pm

Daily Prayer List *(Before you go to sleep tonight, who in your life requires prayer or what circumstance requires prayer today?)*

1. _____   2. _____

3. _____   4. _____

Prayer Focus: 2 Corinthians 6:2   Date: _____

For He says: "In an acceptable time I have heard you, and in the day of salvation I have helped you." Behold, now is the accepted time; behold, now is the day of salvation.

How does this verse speak to your soul, heart, and mind?

_____

_____

_____

Daily Gratitude Prayer *(Consider a prayer like the following each morning before you start your day: Lord, thank you for this day. Lord, I am grateful for my health. Lord, thank you for trusting me to serve your people.)*

_____

_____

_____

Spend Time with God *(How did you spend time with God today? Did you pray, read scripture, or share His word with someone?)*

Daily Activity	Time	Daily Activity	Time
	6:00am		1:00pm
	7:00am		2:00pm
	8:00am		3:00pm
	9:00am		4:00pm
	10:00am		5:00pm
	11:00am		6:00pm
	12:00pm		7:00pm

Daily Prayer List *(Before you go to sleep tonight, who in your life requires prayer or what circumstance requires prayer today?)*

1. _____   2. _____

3. _____   4. _____

Prayer Focus: Micah 7:7   Date: _____

Therefore, I will look to the LORD; I will wait for the God of my salvation; My God will hear me.

How does this verse speak to your soul, heart, and mind?

_____

_____

_____

Daily Gratitude Prayer *(Consider a prayer like the following each morning before you start your day: Lord, thank you for this day. Lord, I am grateful for my health. Lord, thank you for trusting me to serve your people.)*

_____

_____

_____

Spend Time with God *(How did you spend time with God today? Did you pray, read scripture, or share His word with someone?)*

Daily Activity	Time	Daily Activity	Time
	6:00am		1:00pm
	7:00am		2:00pm
	8:00am		3:00pm
	9:00am		4:00pm
	10:00am		5:00pm
	11:00am		6:00pm
	12:00pm		7:00pm

Daily Prayer List *(Before you go to sleep tonight, who in your life requires prayer or what circumstance requires prayer today?)*

1. _____   2. _____

3. _____   4. _____

Prayer Focus: Psalm 116:1-2   Date: _____

I love the LORD, for he heard my voice; he heard my cry for mercy. Because he turned his ear to me, I will call on him as long as I live.

How does this verse speak to your soul, heart, and mind?

_____

_____

_____

Daily Gratitude Prayer *(Consider a prayer like the following each morning before you start your day: Lord, thank you for this day. Lord, I am grateful for my health. Lord, thank you for trusting me to serve your people.)*

_____

_____

_____

Spend Time with God *(How did you spend time with God today? Did you pray, read scripture, or share His word with someone?)*

Daily Activity	Time	Daily Activity	Time
	6:00am		1:00pm
	7:00am		2:00pm
	8:00am		3:00pm
	9:00am		4:00pm
	10:00am		5:00pm
	11:00am		6:00pm
	12:00pm		7:00pm

Daily Prayer List *(Before you go to sleep tonight, who in your life requires prayer or what circumstance requires prayer today?)*

1. _____   2. _____

3. _____   4. _____

Prayer Focus: Deuteronomy 31:8   Date: _____

And the LORD, He is the One who goes before you. He will be with you; He will not leave you nor forsake you; do not fear nor be dismayed.

How does this verse speak to your soul, heart, and mind?

_____

_____

_____

Daily Gratitude Prayer *(Consider a prayer like the following each morning before you start your day: Lord, thank you for this day. Lord, I am grateful for my health. Lord, thank you for trusting me to serve your people.)*

_____

_____

_____

Spend Time with God *(How did you spend time with God today? Did you pray, read scripture, or share His word with someone?)*

Daily Activity	Time	Daily Activity	Time
	6:00am		1:00pm
	7:00am		2:00pm
	8:00am		3:00pm
	9:00am		4:00pm
	10:00am		5:00pm
	11:00am		6:00pm
	12:00pm		7:00pm

Daily Prayer List *(Before you go to sleep tonight, who in your life requires prayer or what circumstance requires prayer today?)*

1. _____   2. _____

3. _____   4. _____

Prayer Focus: 2 Peter 3:18   Date: _____

But grow in the grace and knowledge of our Lord and Savior Jesus Christ. To Him be the glory both now and forever. Amen.

How does this verse speak to your soul, heart, and mind?

_____

_____

_____

Daily Gratitude Prayer *(Consider a prayer like the following each morning before you start your day: Lord, thank you for this day. Lord, I am grateful for my health. Lord, thank you for trusting me to serve your people.)*

_____

_____

_____

Spend Time with God *(How did you spend time with God today? Did you pray, read scripture, or share His word with someone?)*

Daily Activity	Time	Daily Activity	Time
	6:00am		1:00pm
	7:00am		2:00pm
	8:00am		3:00pm
	9:00am		4:00pm
	10:00am		5:00pm
	11:00am		6:00pm
	12:00pm		7:00pm

Daily Prayer List *(Before you go to sleep tonight, who in your life requires prayer or what circumstance requires prayer today?)*

1. _____   2. _____

3. _____   4. _____

Prayer Focus: Ephesians 2:10   Date: _____

For we are His workmanship, created in Christ Jesus for good works, which God prepared beforehand that we should walk in them.

How does this verse speak to your soul, heart, and mind?

_____

_____

_____

Daily Gratitude Prayer *(Consider a prayer like the following each morning before you start your day: Lord, thank you for this day. Lord, I am grateful for my health. Lord, thank you for trusting me to serve your people.)*

_____

_____

_____

Spend Time with God *(How did you spend time with God today? Did you pray, read scripture, or share His word with someone?)*

Daily Activity	Time	Daily Activity	Time
	6:00am		1:00pm
	7:00am		2:00pm
	8:00am		3:00pm
	9:00am		4:00pm
	10:00am		5:00pm
	11:00am		6:00pm
	12:00pm		7:00pm

Daily Prayer List *(Before you go to sleep tonight, who in your life requires prayer or what circumstance requires prayer today?)*

1. _____   2. _____

3. _____   4. _____

Prayer Focus: Colossians 3:23   Date: _____

Whatever you do, work at it with all your heart, as working for the Lord, not for human masters.

How does this verse speak to your soul, heart, and mind?

_____

_____

_____

Daily Gratitude Prayer *(Consider a prayer like the following each morning before you start your day: Lord, thank you for this day. Lord, I am grateful for my health. Lord, thank you for trusting me to serve your people.)*

_____

_____

_____

Spend Time with God *(How did you spend time with God today? Did you pray, read scripture, or share His word with someone?)*

Daily Activity	Time	Daily Activity	Time
	6:00am		1:00pm
	7:00am		2:00pm
	8:00am		3:00pm
	9:00am		4:00pm
	10:00am		5:00pm
	11:00am		6:00pm
	12:00pm		7:00pm

Daily Prayer List *(Before you go to sleep tonight, who in your life requires prayer or what circumstance requires prayer today?)*

1. _____   2. _____

3. _____   4. _____

Prayer Focus: Ephesians 1:23   Date: _____
Which is his body, the fullness of him who fills everything in every way.

How does this verse speak to your soul, heart, and mind?

_____

_____

_____

Daily Gratitude Prayer *(Consider a prayer like the following each morning before you start your day: Lord, thank you for this day. Lord, I am grateful for my health. Lord, thank you for trusting me to serve your people.)*

_____

_____

_____

Spend Time with God *(How did you spend time with God today? Did you pray, read scripture, or share His word with someone?)*

Daily Activity	Time	Daily Activity	Time
	6:00am		1:00pm
	7:00am		2:00pm
	8:00am		3:00pm
	9:00am		4:00pm
	10:00am		5:00pm
	11:00am		6:00pm
	12:00pm		7:00pm

Daily Prayer List *(Before you go to sleep tonight, who in your life requires prayer or what circumstance requires prayer today?)*

1. _____   2. _____

3. _____   4. _____

Prayer Focus: 2 Corinthians 5:21   Date: _____

For He made Him who knew no sin to be sin for us, that we might become the righteousness of God in Him.

How does this verse speak to your soul, heart, and mind?

_____

_____

_____

Daily Gratitude Prayer *(Consider a prayer like the following each morning before you start your day: Lord, thank you for this day. Lord, I am grateful for my health. Lord, thank you for trusting me to serve your people.)*

_____

_____

_____

Spend Time with God *(How did you spend time with God today? Did you pray, read scripture, or share His word with someone?)*

Daily Activity	Time	Daily Activity	Time
	6:00am		1:00pm
	7:00am		2:00pm
	8:00am		3:00pm
	9:00am		4:00pm
	10:00am		5:00pm
	11:00am		6:00pm
	12:00pm		7:00pm

Daily Prayer List (Before you go to sleep tonight, who in your life requires prayer or what circumstance requires prayer today?)

1. _____   2. _____

3. _____   4. _____

Prayer Focus: Psalm 91:1   Date: _____

He who dwells in the secret place of the Most High Shall abide under the shadow of the Almighty.

How does this verse speak to your soul, heart, and mind?

_____

_____

_____

Daily Gratitude Prayer *(Consider a prayer like the following each morning before you start your day: Lord, thank you for this day. Lord, I am grateful for my health. Lord, thank you for trusting me to serve your people.)*

_____

_____

_____

Spend Time with God *(How did you spend time with God today? Did you pray, read scripture, or share His word with someone?)*

Daily Activity	Time	Daily Activity	Time
	6:00am		1:00pm
	7:00am		2:00pm
	8:00am		3:00pm
	9:00am		4:00pm
	10:00am		5:00pm
	11:00am		6:00pm
	12:00pm		7:00pm

Daily Prayer List *(Before you go to sleep tonight, who in your life requires prayer or what circumstance requires prayer today?)*

1. _____   2. _____

3. _____   4. _____

Prayer Focus: Proverbs 22:29   Date: _____

Do you see a man who excels in his work? He will stand before kings; He will not stand before unknown men.

How does this verse speak to your soul, heart, and mind?

_____

_____

_____

Daily Gratitude Prayer *(Consider a prayer like the following each morning before you start your day: Lord, thank you for this day. Lord, I am grateful for my health. Lord, thank you for trusting me to serve your people.)*

_____

_____

_____

Spend Time with God *(How did you spend time with God today? Did you pray, read scripture, or share His word with someone?)*

Daily Activity	Time	Daily Activity	Time
	6:00am		1:00pm
	7:00am		2:00pm
	8:00am		3:00pm
	9:00am		4:00pm
	10:00am		5:00pm
	11:00am		6:00pm
	12:00pm		7:00pm

Daily Prayer List *(Before you go to sleep tonight, who in your life requires prayer or what circumstance requires prayer today?)*

1. _____   2. _____

3. _____   4. _____

Prayer Focus: Romans 8:18   Date: _____

For I consider that the sufferings of this present time are not worthy to be compared with the glory which shall be revealed in us.

How does this verse speak to your soul, heart, and mind?

_____

_____

_____

Daily Gratitude Prayer *(Consider a prayer like the following each morning before you start your day: Lord, thank you for this day. Lord, I am grateful for my health. Lord, thank you for trusting me to serve your people.)*

_____

_____

_____

Spend Time with God *(How did you spend time with God today? Did you pray, read scripture, or share His word with someone?)*

Daily Activity	Time	Daily Activity	Time
	6:00am		1:00pm
	7:00am		2:00pm
	8:00am		3:00pm
	9:00am		4:00pm
	10:00am		5:00pm
	11:00am		6:00pm
	12:00pm		7:00pm

Daily Prayer List *(Before you go to sleep tonight, who in your life requires prayer or what circumstance requires prayer today?)*

1. _____   2. _____

3. _____   4. _____

Prayer Focus: Psalm 37:5   Date: _____

Commit your way to the LORD, trust also in Him, And He shall bring it to pass.

How does this verse speak to your soul, heart, and mind?

_____

_____

_____

Daily Gratitude Prayer *(Consider a prayer like the following each morning before you start your day: Lord, thank you for this day. Lord, I am grateful for my health. Lord, thank you for trusting me to serve your people.)*

_____

_____

_____

Spend Time with God *(How did you spend time with God today? Did you pray, read scripture, or share His word with someone?)*

Daily Activity	Time	Daily Activity	Time
	6:00am		1:00pm
	7:00am		2:00pm
	8:00am		3:00pm
	9:00am		4:00pm
	10:00am		5:00pm
	11:00am		6:00pm
	12:00pm		7:00pm

Daily Prayer List *(Before you go to sleep tonight, who in your life requires prayer or what circumstance requires prayer today?)*

1. _____   2. _____

3. _____   4. _____

Prayer Focus: Hebrews 10:36   Date: _____

For you have need of endurance, so that after you have done the will of God, you may receive the promise.

How does this verse speak to your soul, heart, and mind?

_____

_____

_____

Daily Gratitude Prayer *(Consider a prayer like the following each morning before you start your day: Lord, thank you for this day. Lord, I am grateful for my health. Lord, thank you for trusting me to serve your people.)*

_____

_____

_____

Spend Time with God *(How did you spend time with God today? Did you pray, read scripture, or share His word with someone?)*

Daily Activity	Time	Daily Activity	Time
	6:00am		1:00pm
	7:00am		2:00pm
	8:00am		3:00pm
	9:00am		4:00pm
	10:00am		5:00pm
	11:00am		6:00pm
	12:00pm		7:00pm

Daily Prayer List *(Before you go to sleep tonight, who in your life requires prayer or what circumstance requires prayer today?)*

1. _____   2. _____

3. _____   4. _____

Prayer Focus: 3 John 1:2   Date: _____

Beloved, I pray that you may prosper in all things and be in health, just as your soul prospers.

How does this verse speak to your soul, heart, and mind?

_____

_____

_____

Daily Gratitude Prayer *(Consider a prayer like the following each morning before you start your day: Lord, thank you for this day. Lord, I am grateful for my health. Lord, thank you for trusting me to serve your people.)*

_____

_____

_____

Spend Time with God *(How did you spend time with God today? Did you pray, read scripture, or share His word with someone?)*

Daily Activity	Time	Daily Activity	Time
	6:00am		1:00pm
	7:00am		2:00pm
	8:00am		3:00pm
	9:00am		4:00pm
	10:00am		5:00pm
	11:00am		6:00pm
	12:00pm		7:00pm

Daily Prayer List *(Before you go to sleep tonight, who in your life requires prayer or what circumstance requires prayer today?)*

1. _____   2. _____

3. _____   4. _____

Prayer Focus: 1 John 5:13   Date: _____

I write these things to you who believe in the name of the Son of God so that you may know that you have eternal life.

How does this verse speak to your soul, heart, and mind?

_____

_____

_____

Daily Gratitude Prayer *(Consider a prayer like the following each morning before you start your day: Lord, thank you for this day. Lord, I am grateful for my health. Lord, thank you for trusting me to serve your people.)*

_____

_____

_____

Spend Time with God *(How did you spend time with God today? Did you pray, read scripture, or share His word with someone?)*

Daily Activity	Time	Daily Activity	Time
	6:00am		1:00pm
	7:00am		2:00pm
	8:00am		3:00pm
	9:00am		4:00pm
	10:00am		5:00pm
	11:00am		6:00pm
	12:00pm		7:00pm

Daily Prayer List *(Before you go to sleep tonight, who in your life requires prayer or what circumstance requires prayer today?)*

1. _____   2. _____

3. _____   4. _____

Prayer Focus: Romans 15:13   Date: _____

Now may the God of hope fill you with all joy and peace in believing, so that you will abound in hope by the power of the Holy Spirit.

How does this verse speak to your soul, heart, and mind?

_____

_____

_____

Daily Gratitude Prayer *(Consider a prayer like the following each morning before you start your day: Lord, thank you for this day. Lord, I am grateful for my health. Lord, thank you for trusting me to serve your people.)*

_____

_____

_____

Spend Time with God *(How did you spend time with God today? Did you pray, read scripture, or share His word with someone?)*

Daily Activity	Time	Daily Activity	Time
	6:00am		1:00pm
	7:00am		2:00pm
	8:00am		3:00pm
	9:00am		4:00pm
	10:00am		5:00pm
	11:00am		6:00pm
	12:00pm		7:00pm

Daily Prayer List *(Before you go to sleep tonight, who in your life requires prayer or what circumstance requires prayer today?)*

1. _____ 2. _____

3. _____ 4. _____

Prayer Focus: Proverbs 4:12   Date: _____

When you walk, your steps will not be hindered, and when you run, you will not stumble.

How does this verse speak to your soul, heart, and mind?

_____

_____

_____

Daily Gratitude Prayer *(Consider a prayer like the following each morning before you start your day: Lord, thank you for this day. Lord, I am grateful for my health. Lord, thank you for trusting me to serve your people.)*

_____

_____

_____

Spend Time with God *(How did you spend time with God today? Did you pray, read scripture, or share His word with someone?)*

Daily Activity	Time	Daily Activity	Time
	6:00am		1:00pm
	7:00am		2:00pm
	8:00am		3:00pm
	9:00am		4:00pm
	10:00am		5:00pm
	11:00am		6:00pm
	12:00pm		7:00pm

Daily Prayer List *(Before you go to sleep tonight, who in your life requires prayer or what circumstance requires prayer today?)*

1. _____   2. _____

3. _____   4. _____

Prayer Focus: Proverbs 24:27 (NJKV)   Date: _____

Prepare your outside work, make it fit for yourself in the field; And afterward build your house.

How does this verse speak to your soul, heart, and mind?

_____

_____

_____

Daily Gratitude Prayer *(Consider a prayer like the following each morning before you start your day: Lord, thank you for this day. Lord, I am grateful for my health. Lord, thank you for trusting me to serve your people.)*

_____

_____

_____

Spend Time with God *(How did you spend time with God today? Did you pray, read scripture, or share His word with someone?)*

Daily Activity	Time	Daily Activity	Time
	6:00am		1:00pm
	7:00am		2:00pm
	8:00am		3:00pm
	9:00am		4:00pm
	10:00am		5:00pm
	11:00am		6:00pm
	12:00pm		7:00pm

Daily Prayer List *(Before you go to sleep tonight, who in your life requires prayer or what circumstance requires prayer today?)*

1. _____   2. _____

3. _____   4. _____

Prayer Focus: James 1:19   Date: _____

My dear brothers and sisters, take note of this: Everyone should be quick to listen, slow to speak and slow to become angry.

How does this verse speak to your soul, heart, and mind?

_____

_____

_____

Daily Gratitude Prayer *(Consider a prayer like the following each morning before you start your day: Lord, thank you for this day. Lord, I am grateful for my health. Lord, thank you for trusting me to serve your people.)*

_____

_____

_____

Spend Time with God *(How did you spend time with God today? Did you pray, read scripture, or share His word with someone?)*

Daily Activity	Time	Daily Activity	Time
	6:00am		1:00pm
	7:00am		2:00pm
	8:00am		3:00pm
	9:00am		4:00pm
	10:00am		5:00pm
	11:00am		6:00pm
	12:00pm		7:00pm

Daily Prayer List *(Before you go to sleep tonight, who in your life requires prayer or what circumstance requires prayer today?)*

1. _____   2. _____

3. _____   4. _____

Prayer Focus: James 4:10   Date: _____

Humble yourselves in the sight of the Lord, and He will lift you up.

How does this verse speak to your soul, heart, and mind?

_____

_____

_____

Daily Gratitude Prayer *(Consider a prayer like the following each morning before you start your day: Lord, thank you for this day. Lord, I am grateful for my health. Lord, thank you for trusting me to serve your people.)*

_____

_____

_____

Spend Time with God *(How did you spend time with God today? Did you pray, read scripture, or share His word with someone?)*

Daily Activity	Time	Daily Activity	Time
	6:00am		1:00pm
	7:00am		2:00pm
	8:00am		3:00pm
	9:00am		4:00pm
	10:00am		5:00pm
	11:00am		6:00pm
	12:00pm		7:00pm

Daily Prayer List *(Before you go to sleep tonight, who in your life requires prayer or what circumstance requires prayer today?)*

1. _____   2. _____

3. _____   4. _____

Prayer Focus: Jeremiah 51:20   Date: _____

You are my war club, my weapon for battle— with you I shatter nations, with you I destroy kingdoms.

How does this verse speak to your soul, heart, and mind?

_____

_____

_____

Daily Gratitude Prayer *(Consider a prayer like the following each morning before you start your day: Lord, thank you for this day. Lord, I am grateful for my health. Lord, thank you for trusting me to serve your people.)*

_____

_____

_____

Spend Time with God *(How did you spend time with God today? Did you pray, read scripture, or share His word with someone?)*

Daily Activity	Time	Daily Activity	Time
	6:00am		1:00pm
	7:00am		2:00pm
	8:00am		3:00pm
	9:00am		4:00pm
	10:00am		5:00pm
	11:00am		6:00pm
	12:00pm		7:00pm

Daily Prayer List *(Before you go to sleep tonight, who in your life requires prayer or what circumstance requires prayer today?)*

1. _____   2. _____

3. _____   4. _____

Prayer Focus: Ephesians 6:11   Date: _____

Put on the whole armor of God, that you may be able to stand against the wiles of the devil.

How does this verse speak to your soul, heart, and mind?

_____

_____

_____

Daily Gratitude Prayer *(Consider a prayer like the following each morning before you start your day: Lord, thank you for this day. Lord, I am grateful for my health. Lord, thank you for trusting me to serve your people.)*

_____

_____

_____

Spend Time with God *(How did you spend time with God today? Did you pray, read scripture, or share His word with someone?)*

Daily Activity	Time	Daily Activity	Time
	6:00am		1:00pm
	7:00am		2:00pm
	8:00am		3:00pm
	9:00am		4:00pm
	10:00am		5:00pm
	11:00am		6:00pm
	12:00pm		7:00pm

Daily Prayer List *(Before you go to sleep tonight, who in your life requires prayer or what circumstance requires prayer today?)*

1. _____   2. _____

3. _____   4. _____

Prayer Focus: Psalm 5:3   **Date:** _____

In the morning, LORD, you hear my voice; in the morning I lay my requests before you and wait expectantly.

How does this verse speak to your soul, heart, and mind?

_____

_____

_____

Daily Gratitude Prayer *(Consider a prayer like the following each morning before you start your day: Lord, thank you for this day. Lord, I am grateful for my health. Lord, thank you for trusting me to serve your people.)*

_____

_____

_____

Spend Time with God *(How did you spend time with God today? Did you pray, read scripture, or share His word with someone?)*

Daily Activity	Time	Daily Activity	Time
	6:00am		1:00pm
	7:00am		2:00pm
	8:00am		3:00pm
	9:00am		4:00pm
	10:00am		5:00pm
	11:00am		6:00pm
	12:00pm		7:00pm

Daily Prayer List *(Before you go to sleep tonight, who in your life requires prayer or what circumstance requires prayer today?)*

1. _____   2. _____

3. _____   4. _____

Prayer Focus: Proverbs 18:15   Date: _____

The heart of the discerning acquires knowledge, for the ears of the wise seek it out.

How does this verse speak to your soul, heart, and mind?

_____

_____

_____

Daily Gratitude Prayer *(Consider a prayer like the following each morning before you start your day: Lord, thank you for this day. Lord, I am grateful for my health. Lord, thank you for trusting me to serve your people.)*

_____

_____

_____

Spend Time with God *(How did you spend time with God today? Did you pray, read scripture, or share His word with someone?)*

Daily Activity	Time	Daily Activity	Time
	6:00am		1:00pm
	7:00am		2:00pm
	8:00am		3:00pm
	9:00am		4:00pm
	10:00am		5:00pm
	11:00am		6:00pm
	12:00pm		7:00pm

Daily Prayer List *(Before you go to sleep tonight, who in your life requires prayer or what circumstance requires prayer today?)*

1. _____   2. _____

3. _____   4. _____

Prayer Focus: Mark 5:36   Date: _____

Overhearing what they said, Jesus told him, "Don't be afraid; just believe."

How does this verse speak to your soul, heart, and mind?

_____

_____

_____

Daily Gratitude Prayer *(Consider a prayer like the following each morning before you start your day: Lord, thank you for this day. Lord, I am grateful for my health. Lord, thank you for trusting me to serve your people.)*

_____

_____

_____

Spend Time with God *(How did you spend time with God today? Did you pray, read scripture, or share His word with someone?)*

Daily Activity	Time	Daily Activity	Time
	6:00am		1:00pm
	7:00am		2:00pm
	8:00am		3:00pm
	9:00am		4:00pm
	10:00am		5:00pm
	11:00am		6:00pm
	12:00pm		7:00pm

Daily Prayer List *(Before you go to sleep tonight, who in your life requires prayer or what circumstance requires prayer today?)*

1. _____   2. _____

3. _____   4. _____

Prayer Focus: 1 Corinthians 15:51   Date: _____

Behold, I tell you a mystery: We shall not all sleep, but we shall all be changed.

How does this verse speak to your soul, heart, and mind?

_____

_____

_____

Daily Gratitude Prayer *(Consider a prayer like the following each morning before you start your day: Lord, thank you for this day. Lord, I am grateful for my health. Lord, thank you for trusting me to serve your people.)*

_____

_____

_____

Spend Time with God *(How did you spend time with God today? Did you pray, read scripture, or share His word with someone?)*

Daily Activity	Time	Daily Activity	Time
	6:00am		1:00pm
	7:00am		2:00pm
	8:00am		3:00pm
	9:00am		4:00pm
	10:00am		5:00pm
	11:00am		6:00pm
	12:00pm		7:00pm

Daily Prayer List *(Before you go to sleep tonight, who in your life requires prayer or what circumstance requires prayer today?)*

1. _____   2. _____

3. _____   4. _____

Prayer Focus: John 10:38   Date: _____

"But if I do them, even though you do not believe me, believe the works, that you may know and understand that the Father is in me, and I in the Father."

How does this verse speak to your soul, heart, and mind?

_____

_____

_____

Daily Gratitude Prayer *(Consider a prayer like the following each morning before you start your day: Lord, thank you for this day. Lord, I am grateful for my health. Lord, thank you for trusting me to serve your people.)*

_____

_____

_____

Spend Time with God *(How did you spend time with God today? Did you pray, read scripture, or share His word with someone?)*

Daily Activity	Time	Daily Activity	Time
	6:00am		1:00pm
	7:00am		2:00pm
	8:00am		3:00pm
	9:00am		4:00pm
	10:00am		5:00pm
	11:00am		6:00pm
	12:00pm		7:00pm

Daily Prayer List *(Before you go to sleep tonight, who in your life requires prayer or what circumstance requires prayer today?)*

1. _____   2. _____

3. _____   4. _____

Prayer Focus: Mark 9:23   Date: _____

"'If you can'?" said Jesus. "Everything is possible for one who believes."

How does this verse speak to your soul, heart, and mind?

_____

_____

_____

Daily Gratitude Prayer *(Consider a prayer like the following each morning before you start your day: Lord, thank you for this day. Lord, I am grateful for my health. Lord, thank you for trusting me to serve your people.)*

_____

_____

_____

Spend Time with God *(How did you spend time with God today? Did you pray, read scripture, or share His word with someone?)*

Daily Activity	Time	Daily Activity	Time
	6:00am		1:00pm
	7:00am		2:00pm
	8:00am		3:00pm
	9:00am		4:00pm
	10:00am		5:00pm
	11:00am		6:00pm
	12:00pm		7:00pm

Daily Prayer List *(Before you go to sleep tonight, who in your life requires prayer or what circumstance requires prayer today?)*

1. _____   2. _____

3. _____   4. _____

Prayer Focus: John 15:3   Date: _____

You are already clean because of the word which I have spoken to you.

How does this verse speak to your soul, heart, and mind?

_____

_____

_____

Daily Gratitude Prayer *(Consider a prayer like the following each morning before you start your day: Lord, thank you for this day. Lord, I am grateful for my health. Lord, thank you for trusting me to serve your people.)*

_____

_____

_____

Spend Time with God *(How did you spend time with God today? Did you pray, read scripture, or share His word with someone?)*

Daily Activity	Time	Daily Activity	Time
	6:00am		1:00pm
	7:00am		2:00pm
	8:00am		3:00pm
	9:00am		4:00pm
	10:00am		5:00pm
	11:00am		6:00pm
	12:00pm		7:00pm

Daily Prayer List (Before you go to sleep tonight, who in your life requires prayer or what circumstance requires prayer today?)

1. _____   2. _____

3. _____   4. _____

Prayer Focus: Psalm 73:26   Date: _____

My flesh and my heart fail; But God is the strength of my heart and my portion forever.

How does this verse speak to your soul, heart, and mind?

_____

_____

_____

Daily Gratitude Prayer *(Consider a prayer like the following each morning before you start your day: Lord, thank you for this day. Lord, I am grateful for my health. Lord, thank you for trusting me to serve your people.)*

_____

_____

_____

Spend Time with God *(How did you spend time with God today? Did you pray, read scripture, or share His word with someone?)*

Daily Activity	Time	Daily Activity	Time
	6:00am		1:00pm
	7:00am		2:00pm
	8:00am		3:00pm
	9:00am		4:00pm
	10:00am		5:00pm
	11:00am		6:00pm
	12:00pm		7:00pm

Daily Prayer List *(Before you go to sleep tonight, who in your life requires prayer or what circumstance requires prayer today?)*

1. _____   2. _____

3. _____   4. _____

Prayer Focus: Psalm 31:24   Date: _____

Be of good courage, And He shall strengthen your heart, all you who hope in the LORD.

How does this verse speak to your soul, heart, and mind?

_____

_____

_____

Daily Gratitude Prayer *(Consider a prayer like the following each morning before you start your day: Lord, thank you for this day. Lord, I am grateful for my health. Lord, thank you for trusting me to serve your people.)*

_____

_____

_____

Spend Time with God *(How did you spend time with God today? Did you pray, read scripture, or share His word with someone?)*

Daily Activity	Time	Daily Activity	Time
	6:00am		1:00pm
	7:00am		2:00pm
	8:00am		3:00pm
	9:00am		4:00pm
	10:00am		5:00pm
	11:00am		6:00pm
	12:00pm		7:00pm

Daily Prayer List *(Before you go to sleep tonight, who in your life requires prayer or what circumstance requires prayer today?)*

1. _____   2. _____

3. _____   4. _____

Prayer Focus: Colossians 1:29   Date: _____

To this end I strenuously contend with all the energy Christ so powerfully works in me.

How does this verse speak to your soul, heart, and mind?

_____

_____

_____

Daily Gratitude Prayer *(Consider a prayer like the following each morning before you start your day: Lord, thank you for this day. Lord, I am grateful for my health. Lord, thank you for trusting me to serve your people.)*

_____

_____

_____

Spend Time with God *(How did you spend time with God today? Did you pray, read scripture, or share His word with someone?)*

Daily Activity	Time	Daily Activity	Time
	6:00am		1:00pm
	7:00am		2:00pm
	8:00am		3:00pm
	9:00am		4:00pm
	10:00am		5:00pm
	11:00am		6:00pm
	12:00pm		7:00pm

Daily Prayer List *(Before you go to sleep tonight, who in your life requires prayer or what circumstance requires prayer today?)*

1. _____   2. _____

3. _____   4. _____

Prayer Focus: Galatians 5:1　　　　　Date: _____

It is for freedom that Christ has set us free. Stand firm, then, and do not let yourselves be burdened again by a yoke of slavery.

How does this verse speak to your soul, heart, and mind?

_____

_____

_____

Daily Gratitude Prayer *(Consider a prayer like the following each morning before you start your day: Lord, thank you for this day. Lord, I am grateful for my health. Lord, thank you for trusting me to serve your people.)*

_____

_____

_____

Spend Time with God *(How did you spend time with God today? Did you pray, read scripture, or share His word with someone?)*

Daily Activity	Time	Daily Activity	Time
	6:00am		1:00pm
	7:00am		2:00pm
	8:00am		3:00pm
	9:00am		4:00pm
	10:00am		5:00pm
	11:00am		6:00pm
	12:00pm		7:00pm

Daily Prayer List *(Before you go to sleep tonight, who in your life requires prayer or what circumstance requires prayer today?)*

1. _____   2. _____

3. _____   4. _____

Prayer Focus: Psalm 22:19   Date: _____

But you, LORD, do not be far from me. You are my strength; come quickly to help me.

How does this verse speak to your soul, heart, and mind?

_____

_____

_____

Daily Gratitude Prayer *(Consider a prayer like the following each morning before you start your day: Lord, thank you for this day. Lord, I am grateful for my health. Lord, thank you for trusting me to serve your people.)*

_____

_____

_____

Spend Time with God *(How did you spend time with God today? Did you pray, read scripture, or share His word with someone?)*

Daily Activity	Time	Daily Activity	Time
	6:00am		1:00pm
	7:00am		2:00pm
	8:00am		3:00pm
	9:00am		4:00pm
	10:00am		5:00pm
	11:00am		6:00pm
	12:00pm		7:00pm

Daily Prayer List *(Before you go to sleep tonight, who in your life requires prayer or what circumstance requires prayer today?)*

1. _____   2. _____

3. _____   4. _____

Prayer Focus: 2 Corinthians 6:2   Date: _____

For He says: "In an acceptable time I have heard you, and in the day of salvation I have helped you." Behold, now is the accepted time; behold, now is the day of salvation.

How does this verse speak to your soul, heart, and mind?

_____

_____

_____

Daily Gratitude Prayer *(Consider a prayer like the following each morning before you start your day: Lord, thank you for this day. Lord, I am grateful for my health. Lord, thank you for trusting me to serve your people.)*

_____

_____

_____

Spend Time with God *(How did you spend time with God today? Did you pray, read scripture, or share His word with someone?)*

Daily Activity	Time	Daily Activity	Time
	6:00am		1:00pm
	7:00am		2:00pm
	8:00am		3:00pm
	9:00am		4:00pm
	10:00am		5:00pm
	11:00am		6:00pm
	12:00pm		7:00pm

Daily Prayer List *(Before you go to sleep tonight, who in your life requires prayer or what circumstance requires prayer today?)*

1. _____   2. _____

3. _____   4. _____

Prayer Focus: Psalm 23:1   Date: _____

The LORD is my shepherd; I shall not want.

How does this verse speak to your soul, heart, and mind?

_____

_____

_____

Daily Gratitude Prayer *(Consider a prayer like the following each morning before you start your day: Lord, thank you for this day. Lord, I am grateful for my health. Lord, thank you for trusting me to serve your people.)*

_____

_____

_____

Spend Time with God *(How did you spend time with God today? Did you pray, read scripture, or share His word with someone?)*

Daily Activity	Time	Daily Activity	Time
	6:00am		1:00pm
	7:00am		2:00pm
	8:00am		3:00pm
	9:00am		4:00pm
	10:00am		5:00pm
	11:00am		6:00pm
	12:00pm		7:00pm

Daily Prayer List (Before you go to sleep tonight, who in your life requires prayer or what circumstance requires prayer today?)

1. _____   2. _____

3. _____   4. _____

Prayer Focus: Isaiah 46:4   Date: _____

Even to your old age, I am He, and even to gray hairs I will carry you! I have made, and I will bear; Even I will carry, and will deliver you.

How does this verse speak to your soul, heart, and mind?

_____

_____

_____

Daily Gratitude Prayer *(Consider a prayer like the following each morning before you start your day: Lord, thank you for this day. Lord, I am grateful for my health. Lord, thank you for trusting me to serve your people.)*

_____

_____

_____

Spend Time with God *(How did you spend time with God today? Did you pray, read scripture, or share His word with someone?)*

Daily Activity	Time	Daily Activity	Time
	6:00am		1:00pm
	7:00am		2:00pm
	8:00am		3:00pm
	9:00am		4:00pm
	10:00am		5:00pm
	11:00am		6:00pm
	12:00pm		7:00pm

Daily Prayer List *(Before you go to sleep tonight, who in your life requires prayer or what circumstance requires prayer today?)*

1. _____   2. _____

3. _____   4. _____

Prayer Focus: John 15:7   Date: _____

If you abide in Me, and My words abide in you, you will ask what you desire, and it shall be done for you.

How does this verse speak to your soul, heart, and mind?

_____

_____

_____

Daily Gratitude Prayer *(Consider a prayer like the following each morning before you start your day: Lord, thank you for this day. Lord, I am grateful for my health. Lord, thank you for trusting me to serve your people.)*

_____

_____

_____

Spend Time with God *(How did you spend time with God today? Did you pray, read scripture, or share His word with someone?)*

Daily Activity	Time	Daily Activity	Time
	6:00am		1:00pm
	7:00am		2:00pm
	8:00am		3:00pm
	9:00am		4:00pm
	10:00am		5:00pm
	11:00am		6:00pm
	12:00pm		7:00pm

Daily Prayer List *(Before you go to sleep tonight, who in your life requires prayer or what circumstance requires prayer today?)*

1. _____   2. _____

3. _____   4. _____

Prayer Focus: 1 Corinthians 3:9   Date: _____

For we are co-workers in God's service; you are God's field, God's building.

How does this verse speak to your soul, heart, and mind?

_____

_____

_____

Daily Gratitude Prayer *(Consider a prayer like the following each morning before you start your day: Lord, thank you for this day. Lord, I am grateful for my health. Lord, thank you for trusting me to serve your people.)*

_____

_____

_____

Spend Time with God *(How did you spend time with God today? Did you pray, read scripture, or share His word with someone?)*

Daily Activity	Time	Daily Activity	Time
	6:00am		1:00pm
	7:00am		2:00pm
	8:00am		3:00pm
	9:00am		4:00pm
	10:00am		5:00pm
	11:00am		6:00pm
	12:00pm		7:00pm

Daily Prayer List *(Before you go to sleep tonight, who in your life requires prayer or what circumstance requires prayer today?)*

1. _____   2. _____

3. _____   4. _____

Prayer Focus: Matthew 6:27   Date: _____

Can any one of you by worrying add a single hour to your life?

How does this verse speak to your soul, heart, and mind?

_____

_____

_____

Daily Gratitude Prayer *(Consider a prayer like the following each morning before you start your day: Lord, thank you for this day. Lord, I am grateful for my health. Lord, thank you for trusting me to serve your people.)*

_____

_____

_____

Spend Time with God *(How did you spend time with God today? Did you pray, read scripture, or share His word with someone?)*

Daily Activity	Time	Daily Activity	Time
	6:00am		1:00pm
	7:00am		2:00pm
	8:00am		3:00pm
	9:00am		4:00pm
	10:00am		5:00pm
	11:00am		6:00pm
	12:00pm		7:00pm

Daily Prayer List *(Before you go to sleep tonight, who in your life requires prayer or what circumstance requires prayer today?)*

1. _____   2. _____

3. _____   4. _____

Prayer Focus: Colossians 1:23   Date: _____

If indeed you continue in the faith, grounded and steadfast, and are not moved away from the hope of the gospel which you heard, which was preached to every creature under heaven, of which I, Paul, became a minister.

How does this verse speak to your soul, heart, and mind?

_____

_____

_____

Daily Gratitude Prayer *(Consider a prayer like the following each morning before you start your day: Lord, thank you for this day. Lord, I am grateful for my health. Lord, thank you for trusting me to serve your people.)*

_____

_____

_____

Spend Time with God *(How did you spend time with God today? Did you pray, read scripture, or share His word with someone?)*

Daily Activity	Time	Daily Activity	Time
	6:00am		1:00pm
	7:00am		2:00pm
	8:00am		3:00pm
	9:00am		4:00pm
	10:00am		5:00pm
	11:00am		6:00pm
	12:00pm		7:00pm

Daily Prayer List *(Before you go to sleep tonight, who in your life requires prayer or what circumstance requires prayer today?)*

1. _____   2. _____

3. _____   4. _____

Prayer Focus: Proverbs 31:26   Date: _____

She opens her mouth with wisdom, and on her tongue is the law of kindness.

How does this verse speak to your soul, heart, and mind?

_____

_____

_____

Daily Gratitude Prayer *(Consider a prayer like the following each morning before you start your day: Lord, thank you for this day. Lord, I am grateful for my health. Lord, thank you for trusting me to serve your people.)*

_____

_____

_____

Spend Time with God *(How did you spend time with God today? Did you pray, read scripture, or share His word with someone?)*

Daily Activity	Time	Daily Activity	Time
	6:00am		1:00pm
	7:00am		2:00pm
	8:00am		3:00pm
	9:00am		4:00pm
	10:00am		5:00pm
	11:00am		6:00pm
	12:00pm		7:00pm

Daily Prayer List *(Before you go to sleep tonight, who in your life requires prayer or what circumstance requires prayer today?)*

1. _____   2. _____

3. _____   4. _____

Prayer Focus: Psalm 118:24   Date: _____

This is the day the LORD has made; We will rejoice and be glad in it.

How does this verse speak to your soul, heart, and mind?

_____

_____

_____

Daily Gratitude Prayer *(Consider a prayer like the following each morning before you start your day: Lord, thank you for this day. Lord, I am grateful for my health. Lord, thank you for trusting me to serve your people.)*

_____

_____

_____

Spend Time with God *(How did you spend time with God today? Did you pray, read scripture, or share His word with someone?)*

Daily Activity	Time	Daily Activity	Time
	6:00am		1:00pm
	7:00am		2:00pm
	8:00am		3:00pm
	9:00am		4:00pm
	10:00am		5:00pm
	11:00am		6:00pm
	12:00pm		7:00pm

Daily Prayer List (Before you go to sleep tonight, who in your life requires prayer or what circumstance requires prayer today?)

1. _____   2. _____

3. _____   4. _____

Prayer Focus: 1 Corinthians 3:13   Date: _____

Each one's work will become clear; for the Day will declare it, because it will be revealed by fire; and the fire will test each one's work, of what sort it is.

How does this verse speak to your soul, heart, and mind?

_____

_____

_____

Daily Gratitude Prayer *(Consider a prayer like the following each morning before you start your day: Lord, thank you for this day. Lord, I am grateful for my health. Lord, thank you for trusting me to serve your people.)*

_____

_____

_____

Spend Time with God *(How did you spend time with God today? Did you pray, read scripture, or share His word with someone?)*

Daily Activity	Time	Daily Activity	Time
	6:00am		1:00pm
	7:00am		2:00pm
	8:00am		3:00pm
	9:00am		4:00pm
	10:00am		5:00pm
	11:00am		6:00pm
	12:00pm		7:00pm

Daily Prayer List *(Before you go to sleep tonight, who in your life requires prayer or what circumstance requires prayer today?)*

1. _____   2. _____

3. _____   4. _____

Prayer Focus: 1 Corinthians 12:31   Date: _____

But earnestly desire the best gifts. And yet I show you a more excellent way.

How does this verse speak to your soul, heart, and mind?

_____

_____

_____

Daily Gratitude Prayer *(Consider a prayer like the following each morning before you start your day: Lord, thank you for this day. Lord, I am grateful for my health. Lord, thank you for trusting me to serve your people.)*

_____

_____

_____

Spend Time with God *(How did you spend time with God today? Did you pray, read scripture, or share His word with someone?)*

Daily Activity	Time	Daily Activity	Time
	6:00am		1:00pm
	7:00am		2:00pm
	8:00am		3:00pm
	9:00am		4:00pm
	10:00am		5:00pm
	11:00am		6:00pm
	12:00pm		7:00pm

Daily Prayer List *(Before you go to sleep tonight, who in your life requires prayer or what circumstance requires prayer today?)*

1. _____   2. _____

3. _____   4. _____

Prayer Focus: 2 Thessalonians 3:3   Date: _____

But the Lord is faithful, and he will strengthen you and protect you from the evil one.

How does this verse speak to your soul, heart, and mind?

_____

_____

_____

Daily Gratitude Prayer *(Consider a prayer like the following each morning before you start your day: Lord, thank you for this day. Lord, I am grateful for my health. Lord, thank you for trusting me to serve your people.)*

_____

_____

_____

Spend Time with God *(How did you spend time with God today? Did you pray, read scripture, or share His word with someone?)*

Daily Activity	Time	Daily Activity	Time
	6:00am		1:00pm
	7:00am		2:00pm
	8:00am		3:00pm
	9:00am		4:00pm
	10:00am		5:00pm
	11:00am		6:00pm
	12:00pm		7:00pm

Daily Prayer List *(Before you go to sleep tonight, who in your life requires prayer or what circumstance requires prayer today?)*

1. _____   2. _____

3. _____   4. _____

Prayer Focus: Psalm 3:8   Date: _____

From the LORD comes deliverance. May your blessing be on your people.

How does this verse speak to your soul, heart, and mind?

_____

_____

_____

Daily Gratitude Prayer *(Consider a prayer like the following each morning before you start your day: Lord, thank you for this day. Lord, I am grateful for my health. Lord, thank you for trusting me to serve your people.)*

_____

_____

_____

Spend Time with God *(How did you spend time with God today? Did you pray, read scripture, or share His word with someone?)*

Daily Activity	Time	Daily Activity	Time
	6:00am		1:00pm
	7:00am		2:00pm
	8:00am		3:00pm
	9:00am		4:00pm
	10:00am		5:00pm
	11:00am		6:00pm
	12:00pm		7:00pm

Daily Prayer List (Before you go to sleep tonight, who in your life requires prayer or what circumstance requires prayer today?)

1. _____   2. _____

3. _____   4. _____

Prayer Focus: Ecclesiastes 4:9-10   Date: _____

Two are better than one, because they have a good reward for their labor. For if they fall, one will lift up his companion. But woe to him who is alone when he falls, for he has no one to help him up.

How does this verse speak to your soul, heart, and mind?

_____

_____

_____

Daily Gratitude Prayer *(Consider a prayer like the following each morning before you start your day: Lord, thank you for this day. Lord, I am grateful for my health. Lord, thank you for trusting me to serve your people.)*

_____

_____

_____

Spend Time with God *(How did you spend time with God today? Did you pray, read scripture, or share His word with someone?)*

Daily Activity	Time	Daily Activity	Time
	6:00am		1:00pm
	7:00am		2:00pm
	8:00am		3:00pm
	9:00am		4:00pm
	10:00am		5:00pm
	11:00am		6:00pm
	12:00pm		7:00pm

Daily Prayer List *(Before you go to sleep tonight, who in your life requires prayer or what circumstance requires prayer today?)*

1. _____   2. _____

3. _____   4. _____

Prayer Focus: James 1:4   Date: _____

But let patience have its perfect work, that you may be perfect and complete, lacking nothing.

How does this verse speak to your soul, heart, and mind?

_____

_____

_____

Daily Gratitude Prayer *(Consider a prayer like the following each morning before you start your day: Lord, thank you for this day. Lord, I am grateful for my health. Lord, thank you for trusting me to serve your people.)*

_____

_____

_____

Spend Time with God *(How did you spend time with God today? Did you pray, read scripture, or share His word with someone?)*

Daily Activity	Time	Daily Activity	Time
	6:00am		1:00pm
	7:00am		2:00pm
	8:00am		3:00pm
	9:00am		4:00pm
	10:00am		5:00pm
	11:00am		6:00pm
	12:00pm		7:00pm

Daily Prayer List (Before you go to sleep tonight, who in your life requires prayer or what circumstance requires prayer today?)

1. _____   2. _____

3. _____   4. _____

Prayer Focus: Romans 15:13   Date: _____

Now may the God of hope fill you with all joy and peace in believing, that you may abound in hope by the power of the Holy Spirit.

How does this verse speak to your soul, heart, and mind?

_____

_____

_____

Daily Gratitude Prayer *(Consider a prayer like the following each morning before you start your day: Lord, thank you for this day. Lord, I am grateful for my health. Lord, thank you for trusting me to serve your people.)*

_____

_____

_____

Spend Time with God *(How did you spend time with God today? Did you pray, read scripture, or share His word with someone?)*

Daily Activity	Time	Daily Activity	Time
	6:00am		1:00pm
	7:00am		2:00pm
	8:00am		3:00pm
	9:00am		4:00pm
	10:00am		5:00pm
	11:00am		6:00pm
	12:00pm		7:00pm

Daily Prayer List *(Before you go to sleep tonight, who in your life requires prayer or what circumstance requires prayer today?)*

1. _____   2. _____

3. _____   4. _____

Prayer Focus: Psalm 18:36

Date: _____

You enlarged my path under me, so my feet did not slip.

How does this verse speak to your soul, heart, and mind?

_____

_____

_____

Daily Gratitude Prayer *(Consider a prayer like the following each morning before you start your day: Lord, thank you for this day. Lord, I am grateful for my health. Lord, thank you for trusting me to serve your people.)*

_____

_____

_____

Spend Time with God *(How did you spend time with God today? Did you pray, read scripture, or share His word with someone?)*

Daily Activity	Time	Daily Activity	Time
	6:00am		1:00pm
	7:00am		2:00pm
	8:00am		3:00pm
	9:00am		4:00pm
	10:00am		5:00pm
	11:00am		6:00pm
	12:00pm		7:00pm

Daily Prayer List *(Before you go to sleep tonight, who in your life requires prayer or what circumstance requires prayer today?)*

1. _____

2. _____

3. _____

4. _____

Prayer Focus: 1 Corinthians 9:27   Date: _____

But I discipline my body and bring it into subjection, lest, when I have preached to others, I myself should become disqualified.

How does this verse speak to your soul, heart, and mind?

_____

_____

_____

Daily Gratitude Prayer *(Consider a prayer like the following each morning before you start your day: Lord, thank you for this day. Lord, I am grateful for my health. Lord, thank you for trusting me to serve your people.)*

_____

_____

_____

Spend Time with God *(How did you spend time with God today? Did you pray, read scripture, or share His word with someone?)*

Daily Activity	Time	Daily Activity	Time
	6:00am		1:00pm
	7:00am		2:00pm
	8:00am		3:00pm
	9:00am		4:00pm
	10:00am		5:00pm
	11:00am		6:00pm
	12:00pm		7:00pm

Daily Prayer List (Before you go to sleep tonight, who in your life requires prayer or what circumstance requires prayer today?)

1. _____   2. _____

3. _____   4. _____

Prayer Focus: Romans 8:28   Date: _____

And we know that all things work together for good to those who love God, to those who are the called according to His purpose.

How does this verse speak to your soul, heart, and mind?

_____

_____

_____

Daily Gratitude Prayer *(Consider a prayer like the following each morning before you start your day: Lord, thank you for this day. Lord, I am grateful for my health. Lord, thank you for trusting me to serve your people.)*

_____

_____

_____

Spend Time with God *(How did you spend time with God today? Did you pray, read scripture, or share His word with someone?)*

Daily Activity	Time	Daily Activity	Time
	6:00am		1:00pm
	7:00am		2:00pm
	8:00am		3:00pm
	9:00am		4:00pm
	10:00am		5:00pm
	11:00am		6:00pm
	12:00pm		7:00pm

Daily Prayer List (Before you go to sleep tonight, who in your life requires prayer or what circumstance requires prayer today?)

1. _____   2. _____

3. _____   4. _____

Prayer Focus: Deuteronomy 6:5   Date: _____

You shall love the LORD your God with all your heart, with all your soul, and with all your strength.

How does this verse speak to your soul, heart, and mind?

_____

_____

_____

Daily Gratitude Prayer *(Consider a prayer like the following each morning before you start your day: Lord, thank you for this day. Lord, I am grateful for my health. Lord, thank you for trusting me to serve your people.)*

_____

_____

_____

Spend Time with God *(How did you spend time with God today? Did you pray, read scripture, or share His word with someone?)*

Daily Activity	Time	Daily Activity	Time
	6:00am		1:00pm
	7:00am		2:00pm
	8:00am		3:00pm
	9:00am		4:00pm
	10:00am		5:00pm
	11:00am		6:00pm
	12:00pm		7:00pm

Daily Prayer List *(Before you go to sleep tonight, who in your life requires prayer or what circumstance requires prayer today?)*

1. _____   2. _____

3. _____   4. _____

Prayer Focus: Psalm 46:1   Date: _____

God is our refuge and strength, always ready to help in times of trouble.

How does this verse speak to your soul, heart, and mind?

_____

_____

_____

Daily Gratitude Prayer *(Consider a prayer like the following each morning before you start your day: Lord, thank you for this day. Lord, I am grateful for my health. Lord, thank you for trusting me to serve your people.)*

_____

_____

_____

Spend Time with God *(How did you spend time with God today? Did you pray, read scripture, or share His word with someone?)*

Daily Activity	Time	Daily Activity	Time
	6:00am		1:00pm
	7:00am		2:00pm
	8:00am		3:00pm
	9:00am		4:00pm
	10:00am		5:00pm
	11:00am		6:00pm
	12:00pm		7:00pm

Daily Prayer List *(Before you go to sleep tonight, who in your life requires prayer or what circumstance requires prayer today?)*

1. _____   2. _____

3. _____   4. _____

Prayer Focus: Job 34:4   Date: _____

Let us choose justice for ourselves; Let us know among ourselves what is good.

How does this verse speak to your soul, heart, and mind?

_____

_____

_____

Daily Gratitude Prayer *(Consider a prayer like the following each morning before you start your day: Lord, thank you for this day. Lord, I am grateful for my health. Lord, thank you for trusting me to serve your people.)*

_____

_____

_____

Spend Time with God *(How did you spend time with God today? Did you pray, read scripture, or share His word with someone?)*

Daily Activity	Time	Daily Activity	Time
	6:00am		1:00pm
	7:00am		2:00pm
	8:00am		3:00pm
	9:00am		4:00pm
	10:00am		5:00pm
	11:00am		6:00pm
	12:00pm		7:00pm

Daily Prayer List *(Before you go to sleep tonight, who in your life requires prayer or what circumstance requires prayer today?)*

1. _____   2. _____

3. _____   4. _____

Prayer Focus: Genesis 13:17   Date: _____

Arise, walk in the land through its length and its width, for I give it to you.

How does this verse speak to your soul, heart, and mind?

_____

_____

_____

Daily Gratitude Prayer *(Consider a prayer like the following each morning before you start your day: Lord, thank you for this day. Lord, I am grateful for my health. Lord, thank you for trusting me to serve your people.)*

_____

_____

_____

Spend Time with God *(How did you spend time with God today? Did you pray, read scripture, or share His word with someone?)*

Daily Activity	Time	Daily Activity	Time
	6:00am		1:00pm
	7:00am		2:00pm
	8:00am		3:00pm
	9:00am		4:00pm
	10:00am		5:00pm
	11:00am		6:00pm
	12:00pm		7:00pm

Daily Prayer List (Before you go to sleep tonight, who in your life requires prayer or what circumstance requires prayer today?)

1. _____   2. _____

3. _____   4. _____

Prayer Focus: Ephesians 6:18   Date: _____

And pray in the Spirit on all occasions with all kinds of prayers and requests. With this in mind, be alert and always keep on praying for all the Lord's people.

How does this verse speak to your soul, heart, and mind?

_____

_____

_____

Daily Gratitude Prayer *(Consider a prayer like the following each morning before you start your day: Lord, thank you for this day. Lord, I am grateful for my health. Lord, thank you for trusting me to serve your people.)*

_____

_____

_____

Spend Time with God *(How did you spend time with God today? Did you pray, read scripture, or share His word with someone?)*

Daily Activity	Time	Daily Activity	Time
	6:00am		1:00pm
	7:00am		2:00pm
	8:00am		3:00pm
	9:00am		4:00pm
	10:00am		5:00pm
	11:00am		6:00pm
	12:00pm		7:00pm

Daily Prayer List (Before you go to sleep tonight, who in your life requires prayer or what circumstance requires prayer today?)

1. _____   2. _____

3. _____   4. _____

Prayer Focus: 1 Corinthians 2:5   Date: _____

So that your faith might not rest on human wisdom, but on God's power.

How does this verse speak to your soul, heart, and mind?

_____

_____

_____

Daily Gratitude Prayer *(Consider a prayer like the following each morning before you start your day: Lord, thank you for this day. Lord, I am grateful for my health. Lord, thank you for trusting me to serve your people.)*

_____

_____

_____

Spend Time with God *(How did you spend time with God today? Did you pray, read scripture, or share His word with someone?)*

Daily Activity	Time	Daily Activity	Time
	6:00am		1:00pm
	7:00am		2:00pm
	8:00am		3:00pm
	9:00am		4:00pm
	10:00am		5:00pm
	11:00am		6:00pm
	12:00pm		7:00pm

Daily Prayer List *(Before you go to sleep tonight, who in your life requires prayer or what circumstance requires prayer today?)*

1. _____   2. _____

3. _____   4. _____

Prayer Focus: 1 Peter 2:21   Date: _____

To this you were called, because Christ suffered for you, leaving you an example, that you should follow in his steps.

How does this verse speak to your soul, heart, and mind?

_____

_____

_____

Daily Gratitude Prayer *(Consider a prayer like the following each morning before you start your day: Lord, thank you for this day. Lord, I am grateful for my health. Lord, thank you for trusting me to serve your people.)*

_____

_____

_____

Spend Time with God *(How did you spend time with God today? Did you pray, read scripture, or share His word with someone?)*

Daily Activity	Time	Daily Activity	Time
	6:00am		1:00pm
	7:00am		2:00pm
	8:00am		3:00pm
	9:00am		4:00pm
	10:00am		5:00pm
	11:00am		6:00pm
	12:00pm		7:00pm

Daily Prayer List *(Before you go to sleep tonight, who in your life requires prayer or what circumstance requires prayer today?)*

1. _____   2. _____

3. _____   4. _____

Prayer Focus: Proverbs 3:6-7   Date: _____

In all your ways acknowledge Him, And He shall direct your paths will hear me. Do not be wise in your own eyes; Fear the LORD and depart from evil.

How does this verse speak to your soul, heart, and mind?

_____

_____

_____

Daily Gratitude Prayer *(Consider a prayer like the following each morning before you start your day: Lord, thank you for this day. Lord, I am grateful for my health. Lord, thank you for trusting me to serve your people.)*

_____

_____

_____

Spend Time with God *(How did you spend time with God today? Did you pray, read scripture, or share His word with someone?)*

Daily Activity	Time	Daily Activity	Time
	6:00am		1:00pm
	7:00am		2:00pm
	8:00am		3:00pm
	9:00am		4:00pm
	10:00am		5:00pm
	11:00am		6:00pm
	12:00pm		7:00pm

Daily Prayer List *(Before you go to sleep tonight, who in your life requires prayer or what circumstance requires prayer today?)*

1. _____   2. _____

3. _____   4. _____

Prayer Focus: 2 Corinthians 9:8   Date: _____

And God is able to bless you abundantly, so that in all things at all times, having all that you need, you will abound in every good work.

How does this verse speak to your soul, heart, and mind?

_____

_____

_____

Daily Gratitude Prayer *(Consider a prayer like the following each morning before you start your day: Lord, thank you for this day. Lord, I am grateful for my health. Lord, thank you for trusting me to serve your people.)*

_____

_____

_____

Spend Time with God *(How did you spend time with God today? Did you pray, read scripture, or share His word with someone?)*

Daily Activity	Time	Daily Activity	Time
	6:00am		1:00pm
	7:00am		2:00pm
	8:00am		3:00pm
	9:00am		4:00pm
	10:00am		5:00pm
	11:00am		6:00pm
	12:00pm		7:00pm

Daily Prayer List *(Before you go to sleep tonight, who in your life requires prayer or what circumstance requires prayer today?)*

1. _____   2. _____

3. _____   4. _____

Prayer Focus: Job 17:9   Date: _____

Nevertheless, the righteous will hold to his way, And the one who has clean hands will grow stronger and stronger.

How does this verse speak to your soul, heart, and mind?

_____

_____

_____

Daily Gratitude Prayer *(Consider a prayer like the following each morning before you start your day: Lord, thank you for this day. Lord, I am grateful for my health. Lord, thank you for trusting me to serve your people.)*

_____

_____

_____

Spend Time with God *(How did you spend time with God today? Did you pray, read scripture, or share His word with someone?)*

Daily Activity	Time	Daily Activity	Time
	6:00am		1:00pm
	7:00am		2:00pm
	8:00am		3:00pm
	9:00am		4:00pm
	10:00am		5:00pm
	11:00am		6:00pm
	12:00pm		7:00pm

Daily Prayer List (Before you go to sleep tonight, who in your life requires prayer or what circumstance requires prayer today?)

1. _____   2. _____

3. _____   4. _____

Prayer Focus: 2 Timothy 2:10   Date: _____

Therefore, I endure all things for the sake of the elect, that they also may obtain the salvation which is in Christ Jesus with eternal glory.

How does this verse speak to your soul, heart, and mind?

_____

_____

_____

Daily Gratitude Prayer *(Consider a prayer like the following each morning before you start your day: Lord, thank you for this day. Lord, I am grateful for my health. Lord, thank you for trusting me to serve your people.)*

_____

_____

_____

Spend Time with God *(How did you spend time with God today? Did you pray, read scripture, or share His word with someone?)*

Daily Activity	Time	Daily Activity	Time
	6:00am		1:00pm
	7:00am		2:00pm
	8:00am		3:00pm
	9:00am		4:00pm
	10:00am		5:00pm
	11:00am		6:00pm
	12:00pm		7:00pm

Daily Prayer List (Before you go to sleep tonight, who in your life requires prayer or what circumstance requires prayer today?)

1. _____   2. _____

3. _____   4. _____

Prayer Focus: Romans 4:21   Date: _____

And being fully convinced that what He had promised He was also able to perform.

How does this verse speak to your soul, heart, and mind?

_____

_____

_____

Daily Gratitude Prayer *(Consider a prayer like the following each morning before you start your day: Lord, thank you for this day. Lord, I am grateful for my health. Lord, thank you for trusting me to serve your people.)*

_____

_____

_____

Spend Time with God *(How did you spend time with God today? Did you pray, read scripture, or share His word with someone?)*

Daily Activity	Time	Daily Activity	Time
	6:00am		1:00pm
	7:00am		2:00pm
	8:00am		3:00pm
	9:00am		4:00pm
	10:00am		5:00pm
	11:00am		6:00pm
	12:00pm		7:00pm

Daily Prayer List *(Before you go to sleep tonight, who in your life requires prayer or what circumstance requires prayer today?)*

1. _____   2. _____

3. _____   4. _____

Prayer Focus: Numbers 6:24   Date: _____

The LORD bless you, and keep you; The LORD make His face shine upon you, And be gracious to you.

How does this verse speak to your soul, heart, and mind?

_____

_____

_____

Daily Gratitude Prayer *(Consider a prayer like the following each morning before you start your day: Lord, thank you for this day. Lord, I am grateful for my health. Lord, thank you for trusting me to serve your people.)*

_____

_____

_____

Spend Time with God *(How did you spend time with God today? Did you pray, read scripture, or share His word with someone?)*

Daily Activity	Time	Daily Activity	Time
	6:00am		1:00pm
	7:00am		2:00pm
	8:00am		3:00pm
	9:00am		4:00pm
	10:00am		5:00pm
	11:00am		6:00pm
	12:00pm		7:00pm

Daily Prayer List (Before you go to sleep tonight, who in your life requires prayer or what circumstance requires prayer today?)

1. _____   2. _____

3. _____   4. _____

Prayer Focus: 1 John 5:4   Date: _____

For everyone born of God overcomes the world. This is the victory that has overcome the world, even our faith.

How does this verse speak to your soul, heart, and mind?

_____

_____

_____

Daily Gratitude Prayer *(Consider a prayer like the following each morning before you start your day: Lord, thank you for this day. Lord, I am grateful for my health. Lord, thank you for trusting me to serve your people.)*

_____

_____

_____

Spend Time with God *(How did you spend time with God today? Did you pray, read scripture, or share His word with someone?)*

Daily Activity	Time	Daily Activity	Time
	6:00am		1:00pm
	7:00am		2:00pm
	8:00am		3:00pm
	9:00am		4:00pm
	10:00am		5:00pm
	11:00am		6:00pm
	12:00pm		7:00pm

Daily Prayer List *(Before you go to sleep tonight, who in your life requires prayer or what circumstance requires prayer today?)*

1. _____   2. _____

3. _____   4. _____

Prayer Focus: Psalm 144:1   Date: _____

Praise be to the LORD my Rock, who trains my hands for war, my fingers for battle.

How does this verse speak to your soul, heart, and mind?

_____

_____

_____

Daily Gratitude Prayer *(Consider a prayer like the following each morning before you start your day: Lord, thank you for this day. Lord, I am grateful for my health. Lord, thank you for trusting me to serve your people.)*

_____

_____

_____

Spend Time with God *(How did you spend time with God today? Did you pray, read scripture, or share His word with someone?)*

Daily Activity	Time	Daily Activity	Time
	6:00am		1:00pm
	7:00am		2:00pm
	8:00am		3:00pm
	9:00am		4:00pm
	10:00am		5:00pm
	11:00am		6:00pm
	12:00pm		7:00pm

Daily Prayer List (Before you go to sleep tonight, who in your life requires prayer or what circumstance requires prayer today?)

1. _____   2. _____

3. _____   4. _____

Prayer Focus: 1 Peter 5:10   Date: _____

But may the God of all grace, who called us to His eternal glory by Christ Jesus, after you have suffered a while, perfect, establish, strengthen, and settle you.

How does this verse speak to your soul, heart, and mind?

_____

_____

_____

Daily Gratitude Prayer *(Consider a prayer like the following each morning before you start your day: Lord, thank you for this day. Lord, I am grateful for my health. Lord, thank you for trusting me to serve your people.)*

_____

_____

_____

Spend Time with God *(How did you spend time with God today? Did you pray, read scripture, or share His word with someone?)*

Daily Activity	Time	Daily Activity	Time
	6:00am		1:00pm
	7:00am		2:00pm
	8:00am		3:00pm
	9:00am		4:00pm
	10:00am		5:00pm
	11:00am		6:00pm
	12:00pm		7:00pm

Daily Prayer List (Before you go to sleep tonight, who in your life requires prayer or what circumstance requires prayer today?)

1. _____   2. _____

3. _____   4. _____

Prayer Focus: Hebrews 10:36   Date: _____

You need to persevere so that when you have done the will of God, you will receive what he has promised.

How does this verse speak to your soul, heart, and mind?

_____

_____

_____

Daily Gratitude Prayer *(Consider a prayer like the following each morning before you start your day: Lord, thank you for this day. Lord, I am grateful for my health. Lord, thank you for trusting me to serve your people.)*

_____

_____

_____

Spend Time with God *(How did you spend time with God today? Did you pray, read scripture, or share His word with someone?)*

Daily Activity	Time	Daily Activity	Time
	6:00am		1:00pm
	7:00am		2:00pm
	8:00am		3:00pm
	9:00am		4:00pm
	10:00am		5:00pm
	11:00am		6:00pm
	12:00pm		7:00pm

Daily Prayer List *(Before you go to sleep tonight, who in your life requires prayer or what circumstance requires prayer today?)*

1. _____   2. _____

3. _____   4. _____

Prayer Focus: Colossians 2:7   Date: _____

Rooted and built up in Him and established in the faith, as you have been taught, abounding in it with thanksgiving.

How does this verse speak to your soul, heart, and mind?

_____

_____

_____

Daily Gratitude Prayer *(Consider a prayer like the following each morning before you start your day: Lord, thank you for this day. Lord, I am grateful for my health. Lord, thank you for trusting me to serve your people.)*

_____

_____

_____

Spend Time with God *(How did you spend time with God today? Did you pray, read scripture, or share His word with someone?)*

Daily Activity	Time	Daily Activity	Time
	6:00am		1:00pm
	7:00am		2:00pm
	8:00am		3:00pm
	9:00am		4:00pm
	10:00am		5:00pm
	11:00am		6:00pm
	12:00pm		7:00pm

Daily Prayer List *(Before you go to sleep tonight, who in your life requires prayer or what circumstance requires prayer today?)*

1. _____   2. _____

3. _____   4. _____

Prayer Focus: Philippians 2:13   Date: _____

For it is God who works in you both to will and to do for His good pleasure.

How does this verse speak to your soul, heart, and mind?

_____

_____

_____

Daily Gratitude Prayer *(Consider a prayer like the following each morning before you start your day: Lord, thank you for this day. Lord, I am grateful for my health. Lord, thank you for trusting me to serve your people.)*

_____

_____

_____

Spend Time with God *(How did you spend time with God today? Did you pray, read scripture, or share His word with someone?)*

Daily Activity	Time	Daily Activity	Time
	6:00am		1:00pm
	7:00am		2:00pm
	8:00am		3:00pm
	9:00am		4:00pm
	10:00am		5:00pm
	11:00am		6:00pm
	12:00pm		7:00pm

Daily Prayer List (Before you go to sleep tonight, who in your life requires prayer or what circumstance requires prayer today?)

1. _____   2. _____

3. _____   4. _____

Prayer Focus: Psalm 31:24   Date: _____

Be of good courage, And He shall strengthen your heart, all you who hope in the LORD.

How does this verse speak to your soul, heart, and mind?

_____

_____

_____

Daily Gratitude Prayer *(Consider a prayer like the following each morning before you start your day: Lord, thank you for this day. Lord, I am grateful for my health. Lord, thank you for trusting me to serve your people.)*

_____

_____

_____

Spend Time with God *(How did you spend time with God today? Did you pray, read scripture, or share His word with someone?)*

Daily Activity	Time	Daily Activity	Time
	6:00am		1:00pm
	7:00am		2:00pm
	8:00am		3:00pm
	9:00am		4:00pm
	10:00am		5:00pm
	11:00am		6:00pm
	12:00pm		7:00pm

Daily Prayer List *(Before you go to sleep tonight, who in your life requires prayer or what circumstance requires prayer today?)*

1. _____   2. _____

3. _____   4. _____

Prayer Focus: 1 Corinthians 15:10   Date: _____

But by the grace of God, I am what I am, and his grace to me was not without effect. No, I worked harder than all of them—yet not I, but the grace of God that was with me.

How does this verse speak to your soul, heart, and mind?

_____

_____

_____

Daily Gratitude Prayer *(Consider a prayer like the following each morning before you start your day: Lord, thank you for this day. Lord, I am grateful for my health. Lord, thank you for trusting me to serve your people.)*

_____

_____

_____

Spend Time with God *(How did you spend time with God today? Did you pray, read scripture, or share His word with someone?)*

Daily Activity	Time	Daily Activity	Time
	6:00am		1:00pm
	7:00am		2:00pm
	8:00am		3:00pm
	9:00am		4:00pm
	10:00am		5:00pm
	11:00am		6:00pm
	12:00pm		7:00pm

Daily Prayer List (Before you go to sleep tonight, who in your life requires prayer or what circumstance requires prayer today?)

1. _____   2. _____

3. _____   4. _____

Prayer Focus: Mark 11:23   Date: _____

"Truly I tell you, if anyone says to this mountain, 'Go, throw yourself into the sea,' and does not doubt in their heart but believes that what they say will happen, it will be done for them."

How does this verse speak to your soul, heart, and mind?

_____

_____

_____

Daily Gratitude Prayer *(Consider a prayer like the following each morning before you start your day: Lord, thank you for this day. Lord, I am grateful for my health. Lord, thank you for trusting me to serve your people.)*

_____

_____

_____

Spend Time with God *(How did you spend time with God today? Did you pray, read scripture, or share His word with someone?)*

Daily Activity	Time	Daily Activity	Time
	6:00am		1:00pm
	7:00am		2:00pm
	8:00am		3:00pm
	9:00am		4:00pm
	10:00am		5:00pm
	11:00am		6:00pm
	12:00pm		7:00pm

Daily Prayer List *(Before you go to sleep tonight, who in your life requires prayer or what circumstance requires prayer today?)*

1. _____   2. _____

3. _____   4. _____

Prayer Focus: John 16:24   Date: _____

Until now you have asked nothing in My name. Ask, and you will receive, that your joy may be full.

How does this verse speak to your soul, heart, and mind?

_____

_____

_____

Daily Gratitude Prayer *(Consider a prayer like the following each morning before you start your day: Lord, thank you for this day. Lord, I am grateful for my health. Lord, thank you for trusting me to serve your people.)*

_____

_____

_____

Spend Time with God *(How did you spend time with God today? Did you pray, read scripture, or share His word with someone?)*

Daily Activity	Time	Daily Activity	Time
	6:00am		1:00pm
	7:00am		2:00pm
	8:00am		3:00pm
	9:00am		4:00pm
	10:00am		5:00pm
	11:00am		6:00pm
	12:00pm		7:00pm

Daily Prayer List *(Before you go to sleep tonight, who in your life requires prayer or what circumstance requires prayer today?)*

1. _____   2. _____

3. _____   4. _____

Prayer Focus: Micah 4:13   Date: _____

For behold, I create new heavens and a new earth; And the former shall not be remembered or come to mind.

How does this verse speak to your soul, heart, and mind?

_____

_____

_____

Daily Gratitude Prayer *(Consider a prayer like the following each morning before you start your day: Lord, thank you for this day. Lord, I am grateful for my health. Lord, thank you for trusting me to serve your people.)*

_____

_____

_____

Spend Time with God *(How did you spend time with God today? Did you pray, read scripture, or share His word with someone?)*

Daily Activity	Time	Daily Activity	Time
	6:00am		1:00pm
	7:00am		2:00pm
	8:00am		3:00pm
	9:00am		4:00pm
	10:00am		5:00pm
	11:00am		6:00pm
	12:00pm		7:00pm

Daily Prayer List *(Before you go to sleep tonight, who in your life requires prayer or what circumstance requires prayer today?)*

1. _____   2. _____

3. _____   4. _____

Prayer Focus: 1 Peter 1:3 (NJKV)   Date: _____

Blessed be the God and Father of our Lord Jesus Christ, who according to His abundant mercy has begotten us again to a living hope through the resurrection of Jesus Christ from the dead.

How does this verse speak to your soul, heart, and mind?

_____

_____

_____

Daily Gratitude Prayer *(Consider a prayer like the following each morning before you start your day: Lord, thank you for this day. Lord, I am grateful for my health. Lord, thank you for trusting me to serve your people.)*

_____

_____

_____

Spend Time with God *(How did you spend time with God today? Did you pray, read scripture, or share His word with someone?)*

Daily Activity	Time	Daily Activity	Time
	6:00am		1:00pm
	7:00am		2:00pm
	8:00am		3:00pm
	9:00am		4:00pm
	10:00am		5:00pm
	11:00am		6:00pm
	12:00pm		7:00pm

Daily Prayer List *(Before you go to sleep tonight, who in your life requires prayer or what circumstance requires prayer today?)*

1. _____   2. _____

3. _____   4. _____

Prayer Focus: 1 Peter 5:8   Date: _____

Be sober, be vigilant; because your adversary the devil walks about like a roaring lion, seeking whom he may devour.

How does this verse speak to your soul, heart, and mind?

_____

_____

_____

Daily Gratitude Prayer *(Consider a prayer like the following each morning before you start your day: Lord, thank you for this day. Lord, I am grateful for my health. Lord, thank you for trusting me to serve your people.)*

_____

_____

_____

Spend Time with God *(How did you spend time with God today? Did you pray, read scripture, or share His word with someone?)*

Daily Activity	Time	Daily Activity	Time
	6:00am		1:00pm
	7:00am		2:00pm
	8:00am		3:00pm
	9:00am		4:00pm
	10:00am		5:00pm
	11:00am		6:00pm
	12:00pm		7:00pm

Daily Prayer List *(Before you go to sleep tonight, who in your life requires prayer or what circumstance requires prayer today?)*

1. _____   2. _____

3. _____   4. _____

Prayer Focus: Hebrews 12:1   Date: _____

Therefore, we also, since we are surrounded by so great a cloud of witnesses, let us lay aside every weight, and the sin which so easily ensnares us, and let us run with endurance the race that is set before us.

How does this verse speak to your soul, heart, and mind?

_____

_____

_____

Daily Gratitude Prayer *(Consider a prayer like the following each morning before you start your day: Lord, thank you for this day. Lord, I am grateful for my health. Lord, thank you for trusting me to serve your people.)*

_____

_____

_____

Spend Time with God *(How did you spend time with God today? Did you pray, read scripture, or share His word with someone?)*

Daily Activity	Time	Daily Activity	Time
	6:00am		1:00pm
	7:00am		2:00pm
	8:00am		3:00pm
	9:00am		4:00pm
	10:00am		5:00pm
	11:00am		6:00pm
	12:00pm		7:00pm

Daily Prayer List *(Before you go to sleep tonight, who in your life requires prayer or what circumstance requires prayer today?)*

1. _____   2. _____

3. _____   4. _____

Prayer Focus: 2 Peter 1:3   Date: _____

For His divine power has granted to us everything pertaining to life and godliness, through the true knowledge of Him who called us by His own glory and excellence.

How does this verse speak to your soul, heart, and mind?

_____

_____

_____

Daily Gratitude Prayer *(Consider a prayer like the following each morning before you start your day: Lord, thank you for this day. Lord, I am grateful for my health. Lord, thank you for trusting me to serve your people.)*

_____

_____

_____

Spend Time with God *(How did you spend time with God today? Did you pray, read scripture, or share His word with someone?)*

Daily Activity	Time	Daily Activity	Time
	6:00am		1:00pm
	7:00am		2:00pm
	8:00am		3:00pm
	9:00am		4:00pm
	10:00am		5:00pm
	11:00am		6:00pm
	12:00pm		7:00pm

Daily Prayer List *(Before you go to sleep tonight, who in your life requires prayer or what circumstance requires prayer today?)*

1. _____   2. _____

3. _____   4. _____

Prayer Focus: 2 Corinthians 10:4

Date: _____

For the weapons of our warfare are not carnal but mighty in God for pulling down strongholds.

How does this verse speak to your soul, heart, and mind?

_____

_____

_____

Daily Gratitude Prayer *(Consider a prayer like the following each morning before you start your day: Lord, thank you for this day. Lord, I am grateful for my health. Lord, thank you for trusting me to serve your people.)*

_____

_____

_____

Spend Time with God *(How did you spend time with God today? Did you pray, read scripture, or share His word with someone?)*

Daily Activity	Time	Daily Activity	Time
	6:00am		1:00pm
	7:00am		2:00pm
	8:00am		3:00pm
	9:00am		4:00pm
	10:00am		5:00pm
	11:00am		6:00pm
	12:00pm		7:00pm

Daily Prayer List *(Before you go to sleep tonight, who in your life requires prayer or what circumstance requires prayer today?)*

1. _____   2. _____

3. _____   4. _____

Prayer Focus: Psalm 32:8

Date: _____

I will instruct you and teach you in the way you should go; I will guide you with My eye.

How does this verse speak to your soul, heart, and mind?

_____

_____

_____

Daily Gratitude Prayer *(Consider a prayer like the following each morning before you start your day: Lord, thank you for this day. Lord, I am grateful for my health. Lord, thank you for trusting me to serve your people.)*

_____

_____

_____

Spend Time with God *(How did you spend time with God today? Did you pray, read scripture, or share His word with someone?)*

Daily Activity	Time	Daily Activity	Time
	6:00am		1:00pm
	7:00am		2:00pm
	8:00am		3:00pm
	9:00am		4:00pm
	10:00am		5:00pm
	11:00am		6:00pm
	12:00pm		7:00pm

Daily Prayer List *(Before you go to sleep tonight, who in your life requires prayer or what circumstance requires prayer today?)*

1. _____   2. _____

3. _____   4. _____

Prayer Focus: Isaiah 58:11   Date: _____

The LORD will guide you continually, and satisfy your soul in drought, and strengthen your bones; You shall be like a watered garden, and like a spring of water, whose waters do not fail.

How does this verse speak to your soul, heart, and mind?

_____

_____

_____

Daily Gratitude Prayer *(Consider a prayer like the following each morning before you start your day: Lord, thank you for this day. Lord, I am grateful for my health. Lord, thank you for trusting me to serve your people.)*

_____

_____

_____

Spend Time with God *(How did you spend time with God today? Did you pray, read scripture, or share His word with someone?)*

Daily Activity	Time	Daily Activity	Time
	6:00am		1:00pm
	7:00am		2:00pm
	8:00am		3:00pm
	9:00am		4:00pm
	10:00am		5:00pm
	11:00am		6:00pm
	12:00pm		7:00pm

Daily Prayer List *(Before you go to sleep tonight, who in your life requires prayer or what circumstance requires prayer today?)*

1. _____   2. _____

3. _____   4. _____

Prayer Focus: John 14:12   Date: _____

Most assuredly, I say to you, he who believes in Me, the works that I do he will do also; and greater works than these he will do, because I go to My Father.

How does this verse speak to your soul, heart, and mind?

_____

_____

_____

Daily Gratitude Prayer *(Consider a prayer like the following each morning before you start your day: Lord, thank you for this day. Lord, I am grateful for my health. Lord, thank you for trusting me to serve your people.)*

_____

_____

_____

Spend Time with God *(How did you spend time with God today? Did you pray, read scripture, or share His word with someone?)*

Daily Activity	Time	Daily Activity	Time
	6:00am		1:00pm
	7:00am		2:00pm
	8:00am		3:00pm
	9:00am		4:00pm
	10:00am		5:00pm
	11:00am		6:00pm
	12:00pm		7:00pm

Daily Prayer List (Before you go to sleep tonight, who in your life requires prayer or what circumstance requires prayer today?)

1. _____   2. _____

3. _____   4. _____

Prayer Focus: Psalm 50:15

Date: _____

Call upon Me in the day of trouble; I will deliver you, and you shall glorify Me.

How does this verse speak to your soul, heart, and mind?

_____

_____

_____

Daily Gratitude Prayer *(Consider a prayer like the following each morning before you start your day: Lord, thank you for this day. Lord, I am grateful for my health. Lord, thank you for trusting me to serve your people.)*

_____

_____

_____

Spend Time with God *(How did you spend time with God today? Did you pray, read scripture, or share His word with someone?)*

Daily Activity	Time	Daily Activity	Time
	6:00am		1:00pm
	7:00am		2:00pm
	8:00am		3:00pm
	9:00am		4:00pm
	10:00am		5:00pm
	11:00am		6:00pm
	12:00pm		7:00pm

Daily Prayer List *(Before you go to sleep tonight, who in your life requires prayer or what circumstance requires prayer today?)*

1. _____

2. _____

3. _____

4. _____

Prayer Focus: Ephesians 3:20   Date: _____

Now to Him who is able to do exceedingly abundantly above all that we ask or think, according to the power that works in us.

How does this verse speak to your soul, heart, and mind?

_____

_____

_____

Daily Gratitude Prayer *(Consider a prayer like the following each morning before you start your day: Lord, thank you for this day. Lord, I am grateful for my health. Lord, thank you for trusting me to serve your people.)*

_____

_____

_____

Spend Time with God *(How did you spend time with God today? Did you pray, read scripture, or share His word with someone?)*

Daily Activity	Time	Daily Activity	Time
	6:00am		1:00pm
	7:00am		2:00pm
	8:00am		3:00pm
	9:00am		4:00pm
	10:00am		5:00pm
	11:00am		6:00pm
	12:00pm		7:00pm

Daily Prayer List (Before you go to sleep tonight, who in your life requires prayer or what circumstance requires prayer today?)

1. _____   2. _____

3. _____   4. _____

Prayer Focus: Luke 1:45   Date: _____

Blessed is she who believed, for there will be a fulfillment of those things which were told her from the Lord.

How does this verse speak to your soul, heart, and mind?

_____

_____

_____

Daily Gratitude Prayer *(Consider a prayer like the following each morning before you start your day: Lord, thank you for this day. Lord, I am grateful for my health. Lord, thank you for trusting me to serve your people.)*

_____

_____

_____

Spend Time with God *(How did you spend time with God today? Did you pray, read scripture, or share His word with someone?)*

Daily Activity	Time	Daily Activity	Time
	6:00am		1:00pm
	7:00am		2:00pm
	8:00am		3:00pm
	9:00am		4:00pm
	10:00am		5:00pm
	11:00am		6:00pm
	12:00pm		7:00pm

Daily Prayer List *(Before you go to sleep tonight, who in your life requires prayer or what circumstance requires prayer today?)*

1. _____   2. _____

3. _____   4. _____

Prayer Focus: Philippians 4:6   Date: _____

Be anxious for nothing, but in everything by prayer and supplication, with thanksgiving, let your requests be made known to God.

How does this verse speak to your soul, heart, and mind?

_____

_____

_____

Daily Gratitude Prayer *(Consider a prayer like the following each morning before you start your day: Lord, thank you for this day. Lord, I am grateful for my health. Lord, thank you for trusting me to serve your people.)*

_____

_____

_____

Spend Time with God *(How did you spend time with God today? Did you pray, read scripture, or share His word with someone?)*

Daily Activity	Time	Daily Activity	Time
	6:00am		1:00pm
	7:00am		2:00pm
	8:00am		3:00pm
	9:00am		4:00pm
	10:00am		5:00pm
	11:00am		6:00pm
	12:00pm		7:00pm

Daily Prayer List *(Before you go to sleep tonight, who in your life requires prayer or what circumstance requires prayer today?)*

1. _____ 2. _____

3. _____ 4. _____

Prayer Focus: Psalm 9:10   Date: _____

And those who know Your name will put their trust in You; For You, LORD, have not forsaken those who seek You.

How does this verse speak to your soul, heart, and mind?

_____

_____

_____

Daily Gratitude Prayer *(Consider a prayer like the following each morning before you start your day: Lord, thank you for this day. Lord, I am grateful for my health. Lord, thank you for trusting me to serve your people.)*

_____

_____

_____

Spend Time with God *(How did you spend time with God today? Did you pray, read scripture, or share His word with someone?)*

Daily Activity	Time	Daily Activity	Time
	6:00am		1:00pm
	7:00am		2:00pm
	8:00am		3:00pm
	9:00am		4:00pm
	10:00am		5:00pm
	11:00am		6:00pm
	12:00pm		7:00pm

Daily Prayer List *(Before you go to sleep tonight, who in your life requires prayer or what circumstance requires prayer today?)*

1. _____   2. _____

3. _____   4. _____

Prayer Focus: Exodus 23:20　　　　　Date: _____

Behold, I send an Angel before you to keep you in the way and to bring you into the place which I have prepared.

How does this verse speak to your soul, heart, and mind?

_____

_____

_____

Daily Gratitude Prayer *(Consider a prayer like the following each morning before you start your day: Lord, thank you for this day. Lord, I am grateful for my health. Lord, thank you for trusting me to serve your people.)*

_____

_____

_____

Spend Time with God *(How did you spend time with God today? Did you pray, read scripture, or share His word with someone?)*

Daily Activity	Time	Daily Activity	Time
	6:00am		1:00pm
	7:00am		2:00pm
	8:00am		3:00pm
	9:00am		4:00pm
	10:00am		5:00pm
	11:00am		6:00pm
	12:00pm		7:00pm

Daily Prayer List (Before you go to sleep tonight, who in your life requires prayer or what circumstance requires prayer today?)

1. _____　　2. _____

3. _____　　4. _____

Prayer Focus: Hebrews 6:19   Date: _____

We have this hope as an anchor for the soul, firm and secure. It enters the inner sanctuary behind the curtain.

How does this verse speak to your soul, heart, and mind?

_____

_____

_____

Daily Gratitude Prayer *(Consider a prayer like the following each morning before you start your day: Lord, thank you for this day. Lord, I am grateful for my health. Lord, thank you for trusting me to serve your people.)*

_____

_____

_____

Spend Time with God *(How did you spend time with God today? Did you pray, read scripture, or share His word with someone?)*

Daily Activity	Time	Daily Activity	Time
	6:00am		1:00pm
	7:00am		2:00pm
	8:00am		3:00pm
	9:00am		4:00pm
	10:00am		5:00pm
	11:00am		6:00pm
	12:00pm		7:00pm

Daily Prayer List *(Before you go to sleep tonight, who in your life requires prayer or what circumstance requires prayer today?)*

1. _____   2. _____

3. _____   4. _____

Prayer Focus: Exodus 14:14   Date: _____

The LORD will fight for you, and you shall hold your peace.

How does this verse speak to your soul, heart, and mind?

_____

_____

_____

Daily Gratitude Prayer *(Consider a prayer like the following each morning before you start your day: Lord, thank you for this day. Lord, I am grateful for my health. Lord, thank you for trusting me to serve your people.)*

_____

_____

_____

Spend Time with God *(How did you spend time with God today? Did you pray, read scripture, or share His word with someone?)*

Daily Activity	Time	Daily Activity	Time
	6:00am		1:00pm
	7:00am		2:00pm
	8:00am		3:00pm
	9:00am		4:00pm
	10:00am		5:00pm
	11:00am		6:00pm
	12:00pm		7:00pm

Daily Prayer List *(Before you go to sleep tonight, who in your life requires prayer or what circumstance requires prayer today?)*

1. _____   2. _____

3. _____   4. _____

Prayer Focus: Psalm 89:15   Date: _____

Blessed are those who have learned to acclaim you, who walk in the light of your presence, LORD.

How does this verse speak to your soul, heart, and mind?

_____

_____

_____

Daily Gratitude Prayer *(Consider a prayer like the following each morning before you start your day: Lord, thank you for this day. Lord, I am grateful for my health. Lord, thank you for trusting me to serve your people.)*

_____

_____

_____

Spend Time with God *(How did you spend time with God today? Did you pray, read scripture, or share His word with someone?)*

Daily Activity	Time	Daily Activity	Time
	6:00am		1:00pm
	7:00am		2:00pm
	8:00am		3:00pm
	9:00am		4:00pm
	10:00am		5:00pm
	11:00am		6:00pm
	12:00pm		7:00pm

Daily Prayer List *(Before you go to sleep tonight, who in your life requires prayer or what circumstance requires prayer today?)*

1. _____   2. _____

3. _____   4. _____

Prayer Focus: Isaiah 41:13   Date: _____

For I, the LORD your God, will hold your right hand, saying to you, 'Fear not, I will help you.'

How does this verse speak to your soul, heart, and mind?

_____

_____

_____

Daily Gratitude Prayer *(Consider a prayer like the following each morning before you start your day: Lord, thank you for this day. Lord, I am grateful for my health. Lord, thank you for trusting me to serve your people.)*

_____

_____

_____

Spend Time with God *(How did you spend time with God today? Did you pray, read scripture, or share His word with someone?)*

Daily Activity	Time	Daily Activity	Time
	6:00am		1:00pm
	7:00am		2:00pm
	8:00am		3:00pm
	9:00am		4:00pm
	10:00am		5:00pm
	11:00am		6:00pm
	12:00pm		7:00pm

Daily Prayer List *(Before you go to sleep tonight, who in your life requires prayer or what circumstance requires prayer today?)*

1. _____   2. _____

3. _____   4. _____

Prayer Focus: 1 Peter 2:21   Date: _____

To this you were called, because Christ suffered for you, leaving you an example, that you should follow in his steps.

How does this verse speak to your soul, heart, and mind?

_____

_____

_____

Daily Gratitude Prayer *(Consider a prayer like the following each morning before you start your day: Lord, thank you for this day. Lord, I am grateful for my health. Lord, thank you for trusting me to serve your people.)*

_____

_____

_____

Spend Time with God *(How did you spend time with God today? Did you pray, read scripture, or share His word with someone?)*

Daily Activity	Time	Daily Activity	Time
	6:00am		1:00pm
	7:00am		2:00pm
	8:00am		3:00pm
	9:00am		4:00pm
	10:00am		5:00pm
	11:00am		6:00pm
	12:00pm		7:00pm

Daily Prayer List (Before you go to sleep tonight, who in your life requires prayer or what circumstance requires prayer today?)

1. _____   2. _____

3. _____   4. _____

Prayer Focus: Ephesians 3:12   Date: _____

In him and through faith in him we may approach God with freedom and confidence.

How does this verse speak to your soul, heart, and mind?

_____

_____

_____

Daily Gratitude Prayer *(Consider a prayer like the following each morning before you start your day: Lord, thank you for this day. Lord, I am grateful for my health. Lord, thank you for trusting me to serve your people.)*

_____

_____

_____

Spend Time with God *(How did you spend time with God today? Did you pray, read scripture, or share His word with someone?)*

Daily Activity	Time	Daily Activity	Time
	6:00am		1:00pm
	7:00am		2:00pm
	8:00am		3:00pm
	9:00am		4:00pm
	10:00am		5:00pm
	11:00am		6:00pm
	12:00pm		7:00pm

Daily Prayer List *(Before you go to sleep tonight, who in your life requires prayer or what circumstance requires prayer today?)*

1. _____   2. _____

3. _____   4. _____

Prayer Focus: 1 John 3:1   Date: _____

See what great love the Father has lavished on us, that we should be called children of God! And that is what we are! The reason the world does not know us is that it did not know him.

How does this verse speak to your soul, heart, and mind?

_____

_____

_____

Daily Gratitude Prayer *(Consider a prayer like the following each morning before you start your day: Lord, thank you for this day. Lord, I am grateful for my health. Lord, thank you for trusting me to serve your people.)*

_____

_____

_____

Spend Time with God *(How did you spend time with God today? Did you pray, read scripture, or share His word with someone?)*

Daily Activity	Time	Daily Activity	Time
	6:00am		1:00pm
	7:00am		2:00pm
	8:00am		3:00pm
	9:00am		4:00pm
	10:00am		5:00pm
	11:00am		6:00pm
	12:00pm		7:00pm

Daily Prayer List *(Before you go to sleep tonight, who in your life requires prayer or what circumstance requires prayer today?)*

1. _____   2. _____

3. _____   4. _____

Prayer Focus: 1 Timothy 6:12   Date: _____

Fight the good fight of the faith. Take hold of the eternal life to which you were called when you made your good confession in the presence of many witnesses.

How does this verse speak to your soul, heart, and mind?

_____

_____

_____

Daily Gratitude Prayer *(Consider a prayer like the following each morning before you start your day: Lord, thank you for this day. Lord, I am grateful for my health. Lord, thank you for trusting me to serve your people.)*

_____

_____

_____

Spend Time with God *(How did you spend time with God today? Did you pray, read scripture, or share His word with someone?)*

Daily Activity	Time	Daily Activity	Time
	6:00am		1:00pm
	7:00am		2:00pm
	8:00am		3:00pm
	9:00am		4:00pm
	10:00am		5:00pm
	11:00am		6:00pm
	12:00pm		7:00pm

Daily Prayer List *(Before you go to sleep tonight, who in your life requires prayer or what circumstance requires prayer today?)*

1. _____   2. _____

3. _____   4. _____

Prayer Focus: Genesis 2:7   Date: _____

Then the LORD God formed a man from the dust of the ground and breathed into his nostrils the breath of life, and the man became a living being.

How does this verse speak to your soul, heart, and mind?

_____

_____

_____

Daily Gratitude Prayer *(Consider a prayer like the following each morning before you start your day: Lord, thank you for this day. Lord, I am grateful for my health. Lord, thank you for trusting me to serve your people.)*

_____

_____

_____

Spend Time with God *(How did you spend time with God today? Did you pray, read scripture, or share His word with someone?)*

Daily Activity	Time	Daily Activity	Time
	6:00am		1:00pm
	7:00am		2:00pm
	8:00am		3:00pm
	9:00am		4:00pm
	10:00am		5:00pm
	11:00am		6:00pm
	12:00pm		7:00pm

Daily Prayer List *(Before you go to sleep tonight, who in your life requires prayer or what circumstance requires prayer today?)*

1. _____   2. _____

3. _____   4. _____

Prayer Focus: Philippians 3:15   Date: _____

All of us, then, who are mature should take such a view of things. And if on some point you think differently that too God will make clear to you.

How does this verse speak to your soul, heart, and mind?

_____

_____

_____

Daily Gratitude Prayer *(Consider a prayer like the following each morning before you start your day: Lord, thank you for this day. Lord, I am grateful for my health. Lord, thank you for trusting me to serve your people.)*

_____

_____

_____

Spend Time with God *(How did you spend time with God today? Did you pray, read scripture, or share His word with someone?)*

Daily Activity	Time	Daily Activity	Time
	6:00am		1:00pm
	7:00am		2:00pm
	8:00am		3:00pm
	9:00am		4:00pm
	10:00am		5:00pm
	11:00am		6:00pm
	12:00pm		7:00pm

Daily Prayer List (Before you go to sleep tonight, who in your life requires prayer or what circumstance requires prayer today?)

1. _____   2. _____

3. _____   4. _____

Prayer Focus: 1 Thessalonians 5:11   Date: _____

Therefore encourage one another and build each other up, just as in fact you are doing.

How does this verse speak to your soul, heart, and mind?

_____

_____

_____

Daily Gratitude Prayer *(Consider a prayer like the following each morning before you start your day: Lord, thank you for this day. Lord, I am grateful for my health. Lord, thank you for trusting me to serve your people.)*

_____

_____

_____

Spend Time with God *(How did you spend time with God today? Did you pray, read scripture, or share His word with someone?)*

Daily Activity	Time	Daily Activity	Time
	6:00am		1:00pm
	7:00am		2:00pm
	8:00am		3:00pm
	9:00am		4:00pm
	10:00am		5:00pm
	11:00am		6:00pm
	12:00pm		7:00pm

Daily Prayer List *(Before you go to sleep tonight, who in your life requires prayer or what circumstance requires prayer today?)*

1. _____   2. _____

3. _____   4. _____

Prayer Focus: Romans 6:22   Date: _____

But now having been set free from sin, and having become slaves of God, you have your fruit to holiness, and the end, everlasting life.

How does this verse speak to your soul, heart, and mind?

_____

_____

_____

Daily Gratitude Prayer *(Consider a prayer like the following each morning before you start your day: Lord, thank you for this day. Lord, I am grateful for my health. Lord, thank you for trusting me to serve your people.)*

_____

_____

_____

Spend Time with God *(How did you spend time with God today? Did you pray, read scripture, or share His word with someone?)*

Daily Activity	Time	Daily Activity	Time
	6:00am		1:00pm
	7:00am		2:00pm
	8:00am		3:00pm
	9:00am		4:00pm
	10:00am		5:00pm
	11:00am		6:00pm
	12:00pm		7:00pm

Daily Prayer List *(Before you go to sleep tonight, who in your life requires prayer or what circumstance requires prayer today?)*

1. _____   2. _____

3. _____   4. _____

Prayer Focus: Psalm 138:8   Date: _____

The LORD will perfect that which concerns me; Your mercy,
'O LORD, endures forever; Do not forsake the works of Your hands.

How does this verse speak to your soul, heart, and mind?

_____

_____

_____

Daily Gratitude Prayer *(Consider a prayer like the following each morning before you start your day: Lord, thank you for this day. Lord, I am grateful for my health. Lord, thank you for trusting me to serve your people.)*

_____

_____

_____

Spend Time with God *(How did you spend time with God today? Did you pray, read scripture, or share His word with someone?)*

Daily Activity	Time	Daily Activity	Time
	6:00am		1:00pm
	7:00am		2:00pm
	8:00am		3:00pm
	9:00am		4:00pm
	10:00am		5:00pm
	11:00am		6:00pm
	12:00pm		7:00pm

Daily Prayer List *(Before you go to sleep tonight, who in your life requires prayer or what circumstance requires prayer today?)*

1. _____   2. _____

3. _____   4. _____

Prayer Focus: 1 Thessalonians 5:18

Date: _____

In everything give thanks; for this is the will of God in Christ Jesus for you.

How does this verse speak to your soul, heart, and mind?

_____

_____

_____

Daily Gratitude Prayer *(Consider a prayer like the following each morning before you start your day: Lord, thank you for this day. Lord, I am grateful for my health. Lord, thank you for trusting me to serve your people.)*

_____

_____

_____

Spend Time with God *(How did you spend time with God today? Did you pray, read scripture, or share His word with someone?)*

Daily Activity	Time	Daily Activity	Time
	6:00am		1:00pm
	7:00am		2:00pm
	8:00am		3:00pm
	9:00am		4:00pm
	10:00am		5:00pm
	11:00am		6:00pm
	12:00pm		7:00pm

Daily Prayer List *(Before you go to sleep tonight, who in your life requires prayer or what circumstance requires prayer today?)*

1. _____

2. _____

3. _____

4. _____

Prayer Focus: Colossians 1:29   Date: _____

To this end I also labor, striving according to His working which works in me mightily.

How does this verse speak to your soul, heart, and mind?

_____

_____

_____

Daily Gratitude Prayer *(Consider a prayer like the following each morning before you start your day: Lord, thank you for this day. Lord, I am grateful for my health. Lord, thank you for trusting me to serve your people.)*

_____

_____

_____

Spend Time with God *(How did you spend time with God today? Did you pray, read scripture, or share His word with someone?)*

Daily Activity	Time	Daily Activity	Time
	6:00am		1:00pm
	7:00am		2:00pm
	8:00am		3:00pm
	9:00am		4:00pm
	10:00am		5:00pm
	11:00am		6:00pm
	12:00pm		7:00pm

Daily Prayer List *(Before you go to sleep tonight, who in your life requires prayer or what circumstance requires prayer today?)*

1. _____   2. _____

3. _____   4. _____

Prayer Focus: Lamentations 3:21   Date: _____

Behold, I send an Angel before you to keep you in the way and to bring you into the place which I have prepared.

How does this verse speak to your soul, heart, and mind?

_____

_____

_____

Daily Gratitude Prayer *(Consider a prayer like the following each morning before you start your day: Lord, thank you for this day. Lord, I am grateful for my health. Lord, thank you for trusting me to serve your people.)*

_____

_____

_____

Spend Time with God *(How did you spend time with God today? Did you pray, read scripture, or share His word with someone?)*

Daily Activity	Time	Daily Activity	Time
	6:00am		1:00pm
	7:00am		2:00pm
	8:00am		3:00pm
	9:00am		4:00pm
	10:00am		5:00pm
	11:00am		6:00pm
	12:00pm		7:00pm

Daily Prayer List *(Before you go to sleep tonight, who in your life requires prayer or what circumstance requires prayer today?)*

1. _____   2. _____

3. _____   4. _____

Prayer Focus: Mark 9:24   Date: _____

Immediately the father of the child cried out and said with tears, "Lord, I believe; help my unbelief!"

How does this verse speak to your soul, heart, and mind?

_____

_____

_____

Daily Gratitude Prayer *(Consider a prayer like the following each morning before you start your day: Lord, thank you for this day. Lord, I am grateful for my health. Lord, thank you for trusting me to serve your people.)*

_____

_____

_____

Spend Time with God *(How did you spend time with God today? Did you pray, read scripture, or share His word with someone?)*

Daily Activity	Time	Daily Activity	Time
	6:00am		1:00pm
	7:00am		2:00pm
	8:00am		3:00pm
	9:00am		4:00pm
	10:00am		5:00pm
	11:00am		6:00pm
	12:00pm		7:00pm

Daily Prayer List *(Before you go to sleep tonight, who in your life requires prayer or what circumstance requires prayer today?)*

1. _____   2. _____

3. _____   4. _____

Prayer Focus: Psalm 16:11 (NJKV)   Date: _____

You will show me the path of life; In Your presence is fullness of joy; At Your right hand are pleasures forevermore.

How does this verse speak to your soul, heart, and mind?

_____

_____

_____

Daily Gratitude Prayer *(Consider a prayer like the following each morning before you start your day: Lord, thank you for this day. Lord, I am grateful for my health. Lord, thank you for trusting me to serve your people.)*

_____

_____

_____

Spend Time with God *(How did you spend time with God today? Did you pray, read scripture, or share His word with someone?)*

Daily Activity	Time	Daily Activity	Time
	6:00am		1:00pm
	7:00am		2:00pm
	8:00am		3:00pm
	9:00am		4:00pm
	10:00am		5:00pm
	11:00am		6:00pm
	12:00pm		7:00pm

Daily Prayer List (Before you go to sleep tonight, who in your life requires prayer or what circumstance requires prayer today?)

1. _____   2. _____

3. _____   4. _____

Prayer Focus: 2 Samuel 10:12   Date: _____

Be of good courage and let us be strong for our people and for the cities of our God. And may the LORD do what is good in His sight."

How does this verse speak to your soul, heart, and mind?

_____

_____

_____

Daily Gratitude Prayer *(Consider a prayer like the following each morning before you start your day: Lord, thank you for this day. Lord, I am grateful for my health. Lord, thank you for trusting me to serve your people.)*

_____

_____

_____

Spend Time with God *(How did you spend time with God today? Did you pray, read scripture, or share His word with someone?)*

Daily Activity	Time	Daily Activity	Time
	6:00am		1:00pm
	7:00am		2:00pm
	8:00am		3:00pm
	9:00am		4:00pm
	10:00am		5:00pm
	11:00am		6:00pm
	12:00pm		7:00pm

Daily Prayer List *(Before you go to sleep tonight, who in your life requires prayer or what circumstance requires prayer today?)*

1. _____   2. _____

3. _____   4. _____

Prayer Focus: John 14:1   Date: _____

Let not your heart be troubled; you believe in God, believe also in Me.

How does this verse speak to your soul, heart, and mind?

_____

_____

_____

Daily Gratitude Prayer *(Consider a prayer like the following each morning before you start your day: Lord, thank you for this day. Lord, I am grateful for my health. Lord, thank you for trusting me to serve your people.)*

_____

_____

_____

Spend Time with God *(How did you spend time with God today? Did you pray, read scripture, or share His word with someone?)*

Daily Activity	Time	Daily Activity	Time
	6:00am		1:00pm
	7:00am		2:00pm
	8:00am		3:00pm
	9:00am		4:00pm
	10:00am		5:00pm
	11:00am		6:00pm
	12:00pm		7:00pm

Daily Prayer List *(Before you go to sleep tonight, who in your life requires prayer or what circumstance requires prayer today?)*

1. _____   2. _____

3. _____   4. _____

Prayer Focus: Romans 5:8   Date: _____

But God demonstrates his own love for us in this: While we were still sinners, Christ died for us.

How does this verse speak to your soul, heart, and mind?

_____

_____

_____

Daily Gratitude Prayer *(Consider a prayer like the following each morning before you start your day: Lord, thank you for this day. Lord, I am grateful for my health. Lord, thank you for trusting me to serve your people.)*

_____

_____

_____

Spend Time with God *(How did you spend time with God today? Did you pray, read scripture, or share His word with someone?)*

Daily Activity	Time	Daily Activity	Time
	6:00am		1:00pm
	7:00am		2:00pm
	8:00am		3:00pm
	9:00am		4:00pm
	10:00am		5:00pm
	11:00am		6:00pm
	12:00pm		7:00pm

Daily Prayer List (Before you go to sleep tonight, who in your life requires prayer or what circumstance requires prayer today?)

1. _____   2. _____

3. _____   4. _____

Prayer Focus: 1 Thessalonians 4:4　　　Date: _____

That each of you should learn to control your own body in a way that is holy and honorable.

How does this verse speak to your soul, heart, and mind?

_____

_____

_____

Daily Gratitude Prayer *(Consider a prayer like the following each morning before you start your day: Lord, thank you for this day. Lord, I am grateful for my health. Lord, thank you for trusting me to serve your people.)*

_____

_____

_____

Spend Time with God *(How did you spend time with God today? Did you pray, read scripture, or share His word with someone?)*

Daily Activity	Time	Daily Activity	Time
	6:00am		1:00pm
	7:00am		2:00pm
	8:00am		3:00pm
	9:00am		4:00pm
	10:00am		5:00pm
	11:00am		6:00pm
	12:00pm		7:00pm

Daily Prayer List *(Before you go to sleep tonight, who in your life requires prayer or what circumstance requires prayer today?)*

1. _____　　2. _____

3. _____　　4. _____

Prayer Focus: Romans 8:19   Date: _____

For the earnest expectation of the creation eagerly waits for the revealing of the sons of God.

How does this verse speak to your soul, heart, and mind?

_____

_____

_____

Daily Gratitude Prayer *(Consider a prayer like the following each morning before you start your day: Lord, thank you for this day. Lord, I am grateful for my health. Lord, thank you for trusting me to serve your people.)*

_____

_____

_____

Spend Time with God *(How did you spend time with God today? Did you pray, read scripture, or share His word with someone?)*

Daily Activity	Time	Daily Activity	Time
	6:00am		1:00pm
	7:00am		2:00pm
	8:00am		3:00pm
	9:00am		4:00pm
	10:00am		5:00pm
	11:00am		6:00pm
	12:00pm		7:00pm

Daily Prayer List *(Before you go to sleep tonight, who in your life requires prayer or what circumstance requires prayer today?)*

1. _____   2. _____

3. _____   4. _____

Prayer Focus: Deuteronomy 1:33   Date: _____

Who went ahead of you on your journey, in fire by night and in a cloud by day, to search out places for you to camp and to show you the way you should go.

How does this verse speak to your soul, heart, and mind?

_____

_____

_____

Daily Gratitude Prayer *(Consider a prayer like the following each morning before you start your day: Lord, thank you for this day. Lord, I am grateful for my health. Lord, thank you for trusting me to serve your people.)*

_____

_____

_____

Spend Time with God *(How did you spend time with God today? Did you pray, read scripture, or share His word with someone?)*

Daily Activity	Time	Daily Activity	Time
	6:00am		1:00pm
	7:00am		2:00pm
	8:00am		3:00pm
	9:00am		4:00pm
	10:00am		5:00pm
	11:00am		6:00pm
	12:00pm		7:00pm

Daily Prayer List (Before you go to sleep tonight, who in your life requires prayer or what circumstance requires prayer today?)

1. _____   2. _____

3. _____   4. _____

Prayer Focus: 2 Corinthians 4:18   Date: _____

While we do not look at the things which are seen, but at the things which are not seen. For the things which are seen are temporary, but the things which are not seen are eternal.

How does this verse speak to your soul, heart, and mind?

_____

_____

_____

Daily Gratitude Prayer *(Consider a prayer like the following each morning before you start your day: Lord, thank you for this day. Lord, I am grateful for my health. Lord, thank you for trusting me to serve your people.)*

_____

_____

_____

Spend Time with God *(How did you spend time with God today? Did you pray, read scripture, or share His word with someone?)*

Daily Activity	Time	Daily Activity	Time
	6:00am		1:00pm
	7:00am		2:00pm
	8:00am		3:00pm
	9:00am		4:00pm
	10:00am		5:00pm
	11:00am		6:00pm
	12:00pm		7:00pm

Daily Prayer List (Before you go to sleep tonight, who in your life requires prayer or what circumstance requires prayer today?)

1. _____   2. _____

3. _____   4. _____

Prayer Focus: Psalm 145:15   Date: _____

The eyes of all look expectantly to You, And You give them their food in due season.

How does this verse speak to your soul, heart, and mind?

_____

_____

_____

Daily Gratitude Prayer *(Consider a prayer like the following each morning before you start your day: Lord, thank you for this day. Lord, I am grateful for my health. Lord, thank you for trusting me to serve your people.)*

_____

_____

_____

Spend Time with God *(How did you spend time with God today? Did you pray, read scripture, or share His word with someone?)*

Daily Activity	Time	Daily Activity	Time
	6:00am		1:00pm
	7:00am		2:00pm
	8:00am		3:00pm
	9:00am		4:00pm
	10:00am		5:00pm
	11:00am		6:00pm
	12:00pm		7:00pm

Daily Prayer List (Before you go to sleep tonight, who in your life requires prayer or what circumstance requires prayer today?)

1. _____

2. _____

3. _____

4. _____

Prayer Focus: James 1:2   Date: _____

Consider it pure joy, my brothers, and sisters, whenever you face trials of many kinds.

How does this verse speak to your soul, heart, and mind?

_____

_____

_____

Daily Gratitude Prayer *(Consider a prayer like the following each morning before you start your day: Lord, thank you for this day. Lord, I am grateful for my health. Lord, thank you for trusting me to serve your people.)*

_____

_____

_____

Spend Time with God *(How did you spend time with God today? Did you pray, read scripture, or share His word with someone?)*

Daily Activity	Time	Daily Activity	Time
	6:00am		1:00pm
	7:00am		2:00pm
	8:00am		3:00pm
	9:00am		4:00pm
	10:00am		5:00pm
	11:00am		6:00pm
	12:00pm		7:00pm

Daily Prayer List *(Before you go to sleep tonight, who in your life requires prayer or what circumstance requires prayer today?)*

1. _____   2. _____

3. _____   4. _____

Prayer Focus: 2 Corinthians 9:8   Date: _____

And God is able to bless you abundantly, so that in all things at all times, having all that you need, you will abound in every good work.

How does this verse speak to your soul, heart, and mind?

_____

_____

_____

Daily Gratitude Prayer *(Consider a prayer like the following each morning before you start your day: Lord, thank you for this day. Lord, I am grateful for my health. Lord, thank you for trusting me to serve your people.)*

_____

_____

_____

Spend Time with God *(How did you spend time with God today? Did you pray, read scripture, or share His word with someone?)*

Daily Activity	Time	Daily Activity	Time
	6:00am		1:00pm
	7:00am		2:00pm
	8:00am		3:00pm
	9:00am		4:00pm
	10:00am		5:00pm
	11:00am		6:00pm
	12:00pm		7:00pm

Daily Prayer List (Before you go to sleep tonight, who in your life requires prayer or what circumstance requires prayer today?)

1. _____   2. _____

3. _____   4. _____

Prayer Focus: Galatians 6:10   Date: _____

Therefore, as we have opportunity, let us do good to all, especially to those who are of the household of faith.

How does this verse speak to your soul, heart, and mind?

_____

_____

_____

Daily Gratitude Prayer *(Consider a prayer like the following each morning before you start your day: Lord, thank you for this day. Lord, I am grateful for my health. Lord, thank you for trusting me to serve your people.)*

_____

_____

_____

Spend Time with God *(How did you spend time with God today? Did you pray, read scripture, or share His word with someone?)*

Daily Activity	Time	Daily Activity	Time
	6:00am		1:00pm
	7:00am		2:00pm
	8:00am		3:00pm
	9:00am		4:00pm
	10:00am		5:00pm
	11:00am		6:00pm
	12:00pm		7:00pm

Daily Prayer List *(Before you go to sleep tonight, who in your life requires prayer or what circumstance requires prayer today?)*

1. _____   2. _____

3. _____   4. _____

Prayer Focus: 2 Corinthians 9:7   Date: _____

So let each one give as he purposes in his heart, not grudgingly or of necessity; for God loves a cheerful giver.

How does this verse speak to your soul, heart, and mind?

_____

_____

_____

Daily Gratitude Prayer *(Consider a prayer like the following each morning before you start your day: Lord, thank you for this day. Lord, I am grateful for my health. Lord, thank you for trusting me to serve your people.)*

_____

_____

_____

Spend Time with God *(How did you spend time with God today? Did you pray, read scripture, or share His word with someone?)*

Daily Activity	Time	Daily Activity	Time
	6:00am		1:00pm
	7:00am		2:00pm
	8:00am		3:00pm
	9:00am		4:00pm
	10:00am		5:00pm
	11:00am		6:00pm
	12:00pm		7:00pm

Daily Prayer List *(Before you go to sleep tonight, who in your life requires prayer or what circumstance requires prayer today?)*

1. _____   2. _____

3. _____   4. _____

Prayer Focus: Hebrews 10:36   Date: _____

For you have need of endurance, so that after you have done the will of God, you may receive the promise.

How does this verse speak to your soul, heart, and mind?

_____

_____

_____

Daily Gratitude Prayer *(Consider a prayer like the following each morning before you start your day: Lord, thank you for this day. Lord, I am grateful for my health. Lord, thank you for trusting me to serve your people.)*

_____

_____

_____

Spend Time with God *(How did you spend time with God today? Did you pray, read scripture, or share His word with someone?)*

Daily Activity	Time	Daily Activity	Time
	6:00am		1:00pm
	7:00am		2:00pm
	8:00am		3:00pm
	9:00am		4:00pm
	10:00am		5:00pm
	11:00am		6:00pm
	12:00pm		7:00pm

Daily Prayer List *(Before you go to sleep tonight, who in your life requires prayer or what circumstance requires prayer today?)*

1. _____   2. _____

3. _____   4. _____

Prayer Focus: Colossians 1:10   Date: _____

So that you may live a life worthy of the Lord and please him in every way: bearing fruit in every good work, growing in the knowledge of God.

How does this verse speak to your soul, heart, and mind?

_____

_____

_____

Daily Gratitude Prayer *(Consider a prayer like the following each morning before you start your day: Lord, thank you for this day. Lord, I am grateful for my health. Lord, thank you for trusting me to serve your people.)*

_____

_____

_____

Spend Time with God *(How did you spend time with God today? Did you pray, read scripture, or share His word with someone?)*

Daily Activity	Time	Daily Activity	Time
	6:00am		1:00pm
	7:00am		2:00pm
	8:00am		3:00pm
	9:00am		4:00pm
	10:00am		5:00pm
	11:00am		6:00pm
	12:00pm		7:00pm

Daily Prayer List *(Before you go to sleep tonight, who in your life requires prayer or what circumstance requires prayer today?)*

1. _____   2. _____

3. _____   4. _____

Prayer Focus: 1 Corinthians 13:12   Date: _____

For now, we see only a reflection as in a mirror; then we shall see face to face.
Now I know in part; then I shall know fully, even as I am fully known.

How does this verse speak to your soul, heart, and mind?

_____

_____

_____

Daily Gratitude Prayer *(Consider a prayer like the following each morning before you start your day: Lord, thank you for this day. Lord, I am grateful for my health. Lord, thank you for trusting me to serve your people.)*

_____

_____

_____

Spend Time with God *(How did you spend time with God today? Did you pray, read scripture, or share His word with someone?)*

Daily Activity	Time	Daily Activity	Time
	6:00am		1:00pm
	7:00am		2:00pm
	8:00am		3:00pm
	9:00am		4:00pm
	10:00am		5:00pm
	11:00am		6:00pm
	12:00pm		7:00pm

Daily Prayer List *(Before you go to sleep tonight, who in your life requires prayer or what circumstance requires prayer today?)*

1. _____   2. _____

3. _____   4. _____

Prayer Focus: 1 Corinthians 9:25   Date: _____

Everyone who competes in the games goes into strict training. They do it to get a crown that will not last, but we do it to get a crown that will last forever.

How does this verse speak to your soul, heart, and mind?

_____

_____

_____

Daily Gratitude Prayer *(Consider a prayer like the following each morning before you start your day: Lord, thank you for this day. Lord, I am grateful for my health. Lord, thank you for trusting me to serve your people.)*

_____

_____

_____

Spend Time with God *(How did you spend time with God today? Did you pray, read scripture, or share His word with someone?)*

Daily Activity	Time	Daily Activity	Time
	6:00am		1:00pm
	7:00am		2:00pm
	8:00am		3:00pm
	9:00am		4:00pm
	10:00am		5:00pm
	11:00am		6:00pm
	12:00pm		7:00pm

Daily Prayer List *(Before you go to sleep tonight, who in your life requires prayer or what circumstance requires prayer today?)*

1. _____   2. _____

3. _____   4. _____

Prayer Focus: Judges 6:12   Date: _____

And the angel of the LORD appeared to him and said to him, "The LORD is with you, valiant warrior."

How does this verse speak to your soul, heart, and mind?

_____

_____

_____

Daily Gratitude Prayer *(Consider a prayer like the following each morning before you start your day: Lord, thank you for this day. Lord, I am grateful for my health. Lord, thank you for trusting me to serve your people.)*

_____

_____

_____

Spend Time with God *(How did you spend time with God today? Did you pray, read scripture, or share His word with someone?)*

Daily Activity	Time	Daily Activity	Time
	6:00am		1:00pm
	7:00am		2:00pm
	8:00am		3:00pm
	9:00am		4:00pm
	10:00am		5:00pm
	11:00am		6:00pm
	12:00pm		7:00pm

Daily Prayer List *(Before you go to sleep tonight, who in your life requires prayer or what circumstance requires prayer today?)*

1. _____   2. _____

3. _____   4. _____

Prayer Focus: Luke 6:38   Date: _____

Give, and it will be given to you: good measure, pressed down, shaken together, and running over will be put into your bosom. For with the same measure that you use, it will be measured back to you.

How does this verse speak to your soul, heart, and mind?

_____

_____

_____

Daily Gratitude Prayer *(Consider a prayer like the following each morning before you start your day: Lord, thank you for this day. Lord, I am grateful for my health. Lord, thank you for trusting me to serve your people.)*

_____

_____

_____

Spend Time with God *(How did you spend time with God today? Did you pray, read scripture, or share His word with someone?)*

Daily Activity	Time	Daily Activity	Time
	6:00am		1:00pm
	7:00am		2:00pm
	8:00am		3:00pm
	9:00am		4:00pm
	10:00am		5:00pm
	11:00am		6:00pm
	12:00pm		7:00pm

Daily Prayer List *(Before you go to sleep tonight, who in your life requires prayer or what circumstance requires prayer today?)*

1. _____   2. _____

3. _____   4. _____

Prayer Focus: 1 John 5:4   Date: _____

For whatever is born of God overcomes the world. And this is the victory that has overcome the world— our faith.

How does this verse speak to your soul, heart, and mind?

_____

_____

_____

Daily Gratitude Prayer *(Consider a prayer like the following each morning before you start your day: Lord, thank you for this day. Lord, I am grateful for my health. Lord, thank you for trusting me to serve your people.)*

_____

_____

_____

Spend Time with God *(How did you spend time with God today? Did you pray, read scripture, or share His word with someone?)*

Daily Activity	Time	Daily Activity	Time
	6:00am		1:00pm
	7:00am		2:00pm
	8:00am		3:00pm
	9:00am		4:00pm
	10:00am		5:00pm
	11:00am		6:00pm
	12:00pm		7:00pm

Daily Prayer List (Before you go to sleep tonight, who in your life requires prayer or what circumstance requires prayer today?)

1. _____   2. _____

3. _____   4. _____

Prayer Focus: Proverbs 3:15   Date: _____

She is more precious than rubies, and all the things you may desire cannot compare with her.

How does this verse speak to your soul, heart, and mind?

_____

_____

_____

Daily Gratitude Prayer *(Consider a prayer like the following each morning before you start your day: Lord, thank you for this day. Lord, I am grateful for my health. Lord, thank you for trusting me to serve your people.)*

_____

_____

_____

Spend Time with God *(How did you spend time with God today? Did you pray, read scripture, or share His word with someone?)*

Daily Activity	Time	Daily Activity	Time
	6:00am		1:00pm
	7:00am		2:00pm
	8:00am		3:00pm
	9:00am		4:00pm
	10:00am		5:00pm
	11:00am		6:00pm
	12:00pm		7:00pm

Daily Prayer List (Before you go to sleep tonight, who in your life requires prayer or what circumstance requires prayer today?)

1. _____   2. _____

3. _____   4. _____

Prayer Focus: 1 John 4:16   Date: _____

And so, we know and rely on the love God has for us. God is love. Whoever lives in love lives in God, and God in them.

How does this verse speak to your soul, heart, and mind?

_____

_____

_____

Daily Gratitude Prayer *(Consider a prayer like the following each morning before you start your day: Lord, thank you for this day. Lord, I am grateful for my health. Lord, thank you for trusting me to serve your people.)*

_____

_____

_____

Spend Time with God *(How did you spend time with God today? Did you pray, read scripture, or share His word with someone?)*

Daily Activity	Time	Daily Activity	Time
	6:00am		1:00pm
	7:00am		2:00pm
	8:00am		3:00pm
	9:00am		4:00pm
	10:00am		5:00pm
	11:00am		6:00pm
	12:00pm		7:00pm

Daily Prayer List (Before you go to sleep tonight, who in your life requires prayer or what circumstance requires prayer today?)

1. _____   2. _____

3. _____   4. _____

Prayer Focus: Colossians 3:14   Date: _____

But above all these things put on love, which is the bond of perfection.

How does this verse speak to your soul, heart, and mind?

_____

_____

_____

Daily Gratitude Prayer *(Consider a prayer like the following each morning before you start your day: Lord, thank you for this day. Lord, I am grateful for my health. Lord, thank you for trusting me to serve your people.)*

_____

_____

_____

Spend Time with God *(How did you spend time with God today? Did you pray, read scripture, or share His word with someone?)*

Daily Activity	Time	Daily Activity	Time
	6:00am		1:00pm
	7:00am		2:00pm
	8:00am		3:00pm
	9:00am		4:00pm
	10:00am		5:00pm
	11:00am		6:00pm
	12:00pm		7:00pm

Daily Prayer List (Before you go to sleep tonight, who in your life requires prayer or what circumstance requires prayer today?)

1. _____

2. _____

3. _____

4. _____

Prayer Focus: Isaiah 41:10   Date: _____

Fear not, for I am with you; Be not dismayed, for I am your God. I will strengthen you, Yes, I will help you, I will uphold you with My righteous right hand.'

How does this verse speak to your soul, heart, and mind?

_____

_____

_____

Daily Gratitude Prayer *(Consider a prayer like the following each morning before you start your day: Lord, thank you for this day. Lord, I am grateful for my health. Lord, thank you for trusting me to serve your people.)*

_____

_____

_____

Spend Time with God *(How did you spend time with God today? Did you pray, read scripture, or share His word with someone?)*

Daily Activity	Time	Daily Activity	Time
	6:00am		1:00pm
	7:00am		2:00pm
	8:00am		3:00pm
	9:00am		4:00pm
	10:00am		5:00pm
	11:00am		6:00pm
	12:00pm		7:00pm

Daily Prayer List (Before you go to sleep tonight, who in your life requires prayer or what circumstance requires prayer today?)

1. _____   2. _____

3. _____   4. _____

Prayer Focus: Jeremiah 30:17   Date: _____

But I will restore you to health and heal your wounds,' declares the LORD, 'because you are called an outcast, Zion for whom no one cares.'

How does this verse speak to your soul, heart, and mind?

_____

_____

_____

Daily Gratitude Prayer *(Consider a prayer like the following each morning before you start your day: Lord, thank you for this day. Lord, I am grateful for my health. Lord, thank you for trusting me to serve your people.)*

_____

_____

_____

Spend Time with God *(How did you spend time with God today? Did you pray, read scripture, or share His word with someone?)*

Daily Activity	Time	Daily Activity	Time
	6:00am		1:00pm
	7:00am		2:00pm
	8:00am		3:00pm
	9:00am		4:00pm
	10:00am		5:00pm
	11:00am		6:00pm
	12:00pm		7:00pm

Daily Prayer List *(Before you go to sleep tonight, who in your life requires prayer or what circumstance requires prayer today?)*

1. _____   2. _____

3. _____   4. _____

Prayer Focus: Romans 3:24   Date: _____

Being justified freely by His grace through the redemption that is in Christ Jesus.

How does this verse speak to your soul, heart, and mind?

_____

_____

_____

Daily Gratitude Prayer *(Consider a prayer like the following each morning before you start your day: Lord, thank you for this day. Lord, I am grateful for my health. Lord, thank you for trusting me to serve your people.)*

_____

_____

_____

Spend Time with God *(How did you spend time with God today? Did you pray, read scripture, or share His word with someone?)*

Daily Activity	Time	Daily Activity	Time
	6:00am		1:00pm
	7:00am		2:00pm
	8:00am		3:00pm
	9:00am		4:00pm
	10:00am		5:00pm
	11:00am		6:00pm
	12:00pm		7:00pm

Daily Prayer List *(Before you go to sleep tonight, who in your life requires prayer or what circumstance requires prayer today?)*

1. _____   2. _____

3. _____   4. _____

Prayer Focus: Psalm 30:2

Date: _____

LORD my God, I cried to You for help, and You healed me.

How does this verse speak to your soul, heart, and mind?

_____

_____

_____

Daily Gratitude Prayer *(Consider a prayer like the following each morning before you start your day: Lord, thank you for this day. Lord, I am grateful for my health. Lord, thank you for trusting me to serve your people.)*

_____

_____

_____

Spend Time with God *(How did you spend time with God today? Did you pray, read scripture, or share His word with someone?)*

Daily Activity	Time	Daily Activity	Time
	6:00am		1:00pm
	7:00am		2:00pm
	8:00am		3:00pm
	9:00am		4:00pm
	10:00am		5:00pm
	11:00am		6:00pm
	12:00pm		7:00pm

Daily Prayer List (Before you go to sleep tonight, who in your life requires prayer or what circumstance requires prayer today?)

1. _____

2. _____

3. _____

4. _____

Prayer Focus: Psalm 5:3   Date: _____

In the morning, LORD, you hear my voice; in the morning I lay my requests before you and wait expectantly.

How does this verse speak to your soul, heart, and mind?

_____

_____

_____

Daily Gratitude Prayer *(Consider a prayer like the following each morning before you start your day: Lord, thank you for this day. Lord, I am grateful for my health. Lord, thank you for trusting me to serve your people.)*

_____

_____

_____

Spend Time with God *(How did you spend time with God today? Did you pray, read scripture, or share His word with someone?)*

Daily Activity	Time	Daily Activity	Time
	6:00am		1:00pm
	7:00am		2:00pm
	8:00am		3:00pm
	9:00am		4:00pm
	10:00am		5:00pm
	11:00am		6:00pm
	12:00pm		7:00pm

Daily Prayer List *(Before you go to sleep tonight, who in your life requires prayer or what circumstance requires prayer today?)*

1. _____   2. _____

3. _____   4. _____

Prayer Focus: 1 Corinthians 2:5   Date: _____

So that your faith might not rest on human wisdom, but on God's power.

How does this verse speak to your soul, heart, and mind?

_____

_____

_____

Daily Gratitude Prayer *(Consider a prayer like the following each morning before you start your day: Lord, thank you for this day. Lord, I am grateful for my health. Lord, thank you for trusting me to serve your people.)*

_____

_____

_____

Spend Time with God *(How did you spend time with God today? Did you pray, read scripture, or share His word with someone?)*

Daily Activity	Time	Daily Activity	Time
	6:00am		1:00pm
	7:00am		2:00pm
	8:00am		3:00pm
	9:00am		4:00pm
	10:00am		5:00pm
	11:00am		6:00pm
	12:00pm		7:00pm

Daily Prayer List *(Before you go to sleep tonight, who in your life requires prayer or what circumstance requires prayer today?)*

1. _____   2. _____

3. _____   4. _____

Prayer Focus: Matthew 6:11   Date: _____

Give us this day our daily bread.

How does this verse speak to your soul, heart, and mind?

_____

_____

_____

Daily Gratitude Prayer *(Consider a prayer like the following each morning before you start your day: Lord, thank you for this day. Lord, I am grateful for my health. Lord, thank you for trusting me to serve your people.)*

_____

_____

_____

Spend Time with God *(How did you spend time with God today? Did you pray, read scripture, or share His word with someone?)*

Daily Activity	Time	Daily Activity	Time
	6:00am		1:00pm
	7:00am		2:00pm
	8:00am		3:00pm
	9:00am		4:00pm
	10:00am		5:00pm
	11:00am		6:00pm
	12:00pm		7:00pm

Daily Prayer List (Before you go to sleep tonight, who in your life requires prayer or what circumstance requires prayer today?)

1. _____   2. _____

3. _____   4. _____

Prayer Focus: 1 John 4:18   Date: _____

There is no fear in love; but perfect love casts out fear because fear involves torment. But he who fears has not been made perfect in love.

How does this verse speak to your soul, heart, and mind?

_____

_____

_____

Daily Gratitude Prayer *(Consider a prayer like the following each morning before you start your day: Lord, thank you for this day. Lord, I am grateful for my health. Lord, thank you for trusting me to serve your people.)*

_____

_____

_____

Spend Time with God *(How did you spend time with God today? Did you pray, read scripture, or share His word with someone?)*

Daily Activity	Time	Daily Activity	Time
	6:00am		1:00pm
	7:00am		2:00pm
	8:00am		3:00pm
	9:00am		4:00pm
	10:00am		5:00pm
	11:00am		6:00pm
	12:00pm		7:00pm

Daily Prayer List (Before you go to sleep tonight, who in your life requires prayer or what circumstance requires prayer today?)

1. _____   2. _____

3. _____   4. _____

Prayer Focus: 1 Peter 1:3   Date: _____

Praise be to the God and Father of our Lord Jesus Christ! In his great mercy he has given us new birth into a living hope through the resurrection of Jesus Christ from the dead.

How does this verse speak to your soul, heart, and mind?

_____

_____

_____

Daily Gratitude Prayer *(Consider a prayer like the following each morning before you start your day: Lord, thank you for this day. Lord, I am grateful for my health. Lord, thank you for trusting me to serve your people.)*

_____

_____

_____

Spend Time with God *(How did you spend time with God today? Did you pray, read scripture, or share His word with someone?)*

Daily Activity	Time	Daily Activity	Time
	6:00am		1:00pm
	7:00am		2:00pm
	8:00am		3:00pm
	9:00am		4:00pm
	10:00am		5:00pm
	11:00am		6:00pm
	12:00pm		7:00pm

Daily Prayer List *(Before you go to sleep tonight, who in your life requires prayer or what circumstance requires prayer today?)*

1. _____   2. _____

3. _____   4. _____

Prayer Focus: Jeremiah 17:7   Date: _____

But blessed is the one who trusts in the LORD, whose confidence is in him.

How does this verse speak to your soul, heart, and mind?

_____

_____

_____

Daily Gratitude Prayer *(Consider a prayer like the following each morning before you start your day: Lord, thank you for this day. Lord, I am grateful for my health. Lord, thank you for trusting me to serve your people.)*

_____

_____

_____

Spend Time with God *(How did you spend time with God today? Did you pray, read scripture, or share His word with someone?)*

Daily Activity	Time	Daily Activity	Time
	6:00am		1:00pm
	7:00am		2:00pm
	8:00am		3:00pm
	9:00am		4:00pm
	10:00am		5:00pm
	11:00am		6:00pm
	12:00pm		7:00pm

Daily Prayer List *(Before you go to sleep tonight, who in your life requires prayer or what circumstance requires prayer today?)*

1. _____   2. _____

3. _____   4. _____

Prayer Focus: Proverbs 3:6   Date: _____

In all your ways acknowledge Him, And He shall direct your paths.

How does this verse speak to your soul, heart, and mind?

_____

_____

_____

Daily Gratitude Prayer *(Consider a prayer like the following each morning before you start your day: Lord, thank you for this day. Lord, I am grateful for my health. Lord, thank you for trusting me to serve your people.)*

_____

_____

_____

Spend Time with God *(How did you spend time with God today? Did you pray, read scripture, or share His word with someone?)*

Daily Activity	Time	Daily Activity	Time
	6:00am		1:00pm
	7:00am		2:00pm
	8:00am		3:00pm
	9:00am		4:00pm
	10:00am		5:00pm
	11:00am		6:00pm
	12:00pm		7:00pm

Daily Prayer List *(Before you go to sleep tonight, who in your life requires prayer or what circumstance requires prayer today?)*

1. _____   2. _____

3. _____   4. _____

Prayer Focus: 2 Corinthians 4:17 Date: _____

For our light affliction, which is but for a moment, is working for us a far more exceeding and eternal weight of glory.

How does this verse speak to your soul, heart, and mind?

_____

_____

_____

Daily Gratitude Prayer *(Consider a prayer like the following each morning before you start your day: Lord, thank you for this day. Lord, I am grateful for my health. Lord, thank you for trusting me to serve your people.)*

_____

_____

_____

Spend Time with God *(How did you spend time with God today? Did you pray, read scripture, or share His word with someone?)*

Daily Activity	Time	Daily Activity	Time
	6:00am		1:00pm
	7:00am		2:00pm
	8:00am		3:00pm
	9:00am		4:00pm
	10:00am		5:00pm
	11:00am		6:00pm
	12:00pm		7:00pm

Daily Prayer List (Before you go to sleep tonight, who in your life requires prayer or what circumstance requires prayer today?)

1. _____   2. _____

3. _____   4. _____

Prayer Focus: 1 John 5:4   Date: _____

For everyone born of God overcomes the world. This is the victory that has overcome the world, even our faith.

How does this verse speak to your soul, heart, and mind?

_____

_____

_____

Daily Gratitude Prayer *(Consider a prayer like the following each morning before you start your day: Lord, thank you for this day. Lord, I am grateful for my health. Lord, thank you for trusting me to serve your people.)*

_____

_____

_____

Spend Time with God *(How did you spend time with God today? Did you pray, read scripture, or share His word with someone?)*

Daily Activity	Time	Daily Activity	Time
	6:00am		1:00pm
	7:00am		2:00pm
	8:00am		3:00pm
	9:00am		4:00pm
	10:00am		5:00pm
	11:00am		6:00pm
	12:00pm		7:00pm

Daily Prayer List (Before you go to sleep tonight, who in your life requires prayer or what circumstance requires prayer today?)

1. _____   2. _____

3. _____   4. _____

Prayer Focus: Job 23:11   Date: _____

My foot has held fast to His steps; I have kept His way and not turned aside.

How does this verse speak to your soul, heart, and mind?

_____

_____

_____

Daily Gratitude Prayer *(Consider a prayer like the following each morning before you start your day: Lord, thank you for this day. Lord, I am grateful for my health. Lord, thank you for trusting me to serve your people.)*

_____

_____

_____

Spend Time with God *(How did you spend time with God today? Did you pray, read scripture, or share His word with someone?)*

Daily Activity	Time	Daily Activity	Time
	6:00am		1:00pm
	7:00am		2:00pm
	8:00am		3:00pm
	9:00am		4:00pm
	10:00am		5:00pm
	11:00am		6:00pm
	12:00pm		7:00pm

Daily Prayer List *(Before you go to sleep tonight, who in your life requires prayer or what circumstance requires prayer today?)*

1. _____   2. _____

3. _____   4. _____

Prayer Focus: Psalm 4:8   Date: _____

In peace I will lie down and sleep, for you alone, LORD, make me dwell in safety.

How does this verse speak to your soul, heart, and mind?

_____

_____

_____

Daily Gratitude Prayer *(Consider a prayer like the following each morning before you start your day: Lord, thank you for this day. Lord, I am grateful for my health. Lord, thank you for trusting me to serve your people.)*

_____

_____

_____

Spend Time with God *(How did you spend time with God today? Did you pray, read scripture, or share His word with someone?)*

Daily Activity	Time	Daily Activity	Time
	6:00am		1:00pm
	7:00am		2:00pm
	8:00am		3:00pm
	9:00am		4:00pm
	10:00am		5:00pm
	11:00am		6:00pm
	12:00pm		7:00pm

Daily Prayer List *(Before you go to sleep tonight, who in your life requires prayer or what circumstance requires prayer today?)*

1. _____   2. _____

3. _____   4. _____

Prayer Focus: Philippians 4:7　　　Date: _____

And the peace of God, which surpasses all understanding, will guard your hearts and minds through Christ Jesus.

How does this verse speak to your soul, heart, and mind?

_____

_____

_____

Daily Gratitude Prayer *(Consider a prayer like the following each morning before you start your day: Lord, thank you for this day. Lord, I am grateful for my health. Lord, thank you for trusting me to serve your people.)*

_____

_____

_____

Spend Time with God *(How did you spend time with God today? Did you pray, read scripture, or share His word with someone?)*

Daily Activity	Time	Daily Activity	Time
	6:00am		1:00pm
	7:00am		2:00pm
	8:00am		3:00pm
	9:00am		4:00pm
	10:00am		5:00pm
	11:00am		6:00pm
	12:00pm		7:00pm

Daily Prayer List *(Before you go to sleep tonight, who in your life requires prayer or what circumstance requires prayer today?)*

1. _____   2. _____

3. _____   4. _____

Prayer Focus: Colossians 4:5   Date: _____

Conduct yourselves with wisdom toward outsiders, making the most of the opportunity.

How does this verse speak to your soul, heart, and mind?

_____

_____

_____

Daily Gratitude Prayer *(Consider a prayer like the following each morning before you start your day: Lord, thank you for this day. Lord, I am grateful for my health. Lord, thank you for trusting me to serve your people.)*

_____

_____

_____

Spend Time with God *(How did you spend time with God today? Did you pray, read scripture, or share His word with someone?)*

Daily Activity	Time	Daily Activity	Time
	6:00am		1:00pm
	7:00am		2:00pm
	8:00am		3:00pm
	9:00am		4:00pm
	10:00am		5:00pm
	11:00am		6:00pm
	12:00pm		7:00pm

Daily Prayer List *(Before you go to sleep tonight, who in your life requires prayer or what circumstance requires prayer today?)*

1. _____   2. _____

3. _____   4. _____

Prayer Focus: Hebrews 10:36   **Date:** _____

You need to persevere so that when you have done the will of God, you will receive what he has promised.

How does this verse speak to your soul, heart, and mind?

_____

_____

_____

Daily Gratitude Prayer *(Consider a prayer like the following each morning before you start your day: Lord, thank you for this day. Lord, I am grateful for my health. Lord, thank you for trusting me to serve your people.)*

_____

_____

_____

Spend Time with God *(How did you spend time with God today? Did you pray, read scripture, or share His word with someone?)*

Daily Activity	Time	Daily Activity	Time
	6:00am		1:00pm
	7:00am		2:00pm
	8:00am		3:00pm
	9:00am		4:00pm
	10:00am		5:00pm
	11:00am		6:00pm
	12:00pm		7:00pm

Daily Prayer List (Before you go to sleep tonight, who in your life requires prayer or what circumstance requires prayer today?)

1. _____   2. _____

3. _____   4. _____

Prayer Focus: Proverbs 4:12   Date: _____

When you walk, your steps will not be hampered; when you run, you will not stumble.

How does this verse speak to your soul, heart, and mind?

_____

_____

_____

Daily Gratitude Prayer *(Consider a prayer like the following each morning before you start your day: Lord, thank you for this day. Lord, I am grateful for my health. Lord, thank you for trusting me to serve your people.)*

_____

_____

_____

Spend Time with God *(How did you spend time with God today? Did you pray, read scripture, or share His word with someone?)*

Daily Activity	Time	Daily Activity	Time
	6:00am		1:00pm
	7:00am		2:00pm
	8:00am		3:00pm
	9:00am		4:00pm
	10:00am		5:00pm
	11:00am		6:00pm
	12:00pm		7:00pm

Daily Prayer List (Before you go to sleep tonight, who in your life requires prayer or what circumstance requires prayer today?)

1. _____   2. _____

3. _____   4. _____

Prayer Focus: Romans 8:31   Date: _____

What, then, shall we say in response to these things? If God is for us, who can be against us?

How does this verse speak to your soul, heart, and mind?

_____

_____

_____

Daily Gratitude Prayer *(Consider a prayer like the following each morning before you start your day: Lord, thank you for this day. Lord, I am grateful for my health. Lord, thank you for trusting me to serve your people.)*

_____

_____

_____

Spend Time with God *(How did you spend time with God today? Did you pray, read scripture, or share His word with someone?)*

Daily Activity	Time	Daily Activity	Time
	6:00am		1:00pm
	7:00am		2:00pm
	8:00am		3:00pm
	9:00am		4:00pm
	10:00am		5:00pm
	11:00am		6:00pm
	12:00pm		7:00pm

Daily Prayer List (Before you go to sleep tonight, who in your life requires prayer or what circumstance requires prayer today?)

1. _____   2. _____

3. _____   4. _____

Prayer Focus: Galatians 5:1   Date: _____

Stand fast therefore in the liberty by which Christ has made us free, and do not be entangled again with a yoke of bondage.

How does this verse speak to your soul, heart, and mind?

_____

_____

_____

Daily Gratitude Prayer *(Consider a prayer like the following each morning before you start your day: Lord, thank you for this day. Lord, I am grateful for my health. Lord, thank you for trusting me to serve your people.)*

_____

_____

_____

Spend Time with God *(How did you spend time with God today? Did you pray, read scripture, or share His word with someone?)*

Daily Activity	Time	Daily Activity	Time
	6:00am		1:00pm
	7:00am		2:00pm
	8:00am		3:00pm
	9:00am		4:00pm
	10:00am		5:00pm
	11:00am		6:00pm
	12:00pm		7:00pm

Daily Prayer List (Before you go to sleep tonight, who in your life requires prayer or what circumstance requires prayer today?)

1. _____   2. _____

3. _____   4. _____

Prayer Focus: Psalm 90:17   Date: _____

May the kindness of the Lord our God be upon us; And confirm for us the work of our hands; Yes, confirm the work of our hands.

How does this verse speak to your soul, heart, and mind?

_____

_____

_____

Daily Gratitude Prayer *(Consider a prayer like the following each morning before you start your day: Lord, thank you for this day. Lord, I am grateful for my health. Lord, thank you for trusting me to serve your people.)*

_____

_____

_____

Spend Time with God *(How did you spend time with God today? Did you pray, read scripture, or share His word with someone?)*

Daily Activity	Time	Daily Activity	Time
	6:00am		1:00pm
	7:00am		2:00pm
	8:00am		3:00pm
	9:00am		4:00pm
	10:00am		5:00pm
	11:00am		6:00pm
	12:00pm		7:00pm

Daily Prayer List *(Before you go to sleep tonight, who in your life requires prayer or what circumstance requires prayer today?)*

1. _____   2. _____

3. _____   4. _____

Prayer Focus: Proverbs 15:1   Date: _____

A gentle answer turns away wrath, but a harsh word stirs up anger.

How does this verse speak to your soul, heart, and mind?

_____

_____

_____

Daily Gratitude Prayer *(Consider a prayer like the following each morning before you start your day: Lord, thank you for this day. Lord, I am grateful for my health. Lord, thank you for trusting me to serve your people.)*

_____

_____

_____

Spend Time with God *(How did you spend time with God today? Did you pray, read scripture, or share His word with someone?)*

Daily Activity	Time	Daily Activity	Time
	6:00am		1:00pm
	7:00am		2:00pm
	8:00am		3:00pm
	9:00am		4:00pm
	10:00am		5:00pm
	11:00am		6:00pm
	12:00pm		7:00pm

Daily Prayer List *(Before you go to sleep tonight, who in your life requires prayer or what circumstance requires prayer today?)*

1. _____   2. _____

3. _____   4. _____

Prayer Focus: Romans 13:8   Date: _____

Owe no one anything except to love one another, for he who loves another has fulfilled the law.

How does this verse speak to your soul, heart, and mind?

_____

_____

_____

Daily Gratitude Prayer *(Consider a prayer like the following each morning before you start your day: Lord, thank you for this day. Lord, I am grateful for my health. Lord, thank you for trusting me to serve your people.)*

_____

_____

_____

Spend Time with God *(How did you spend time with God today? Did you pray, read scripture, or share His word with someone?)*

Daily Activity	Time	Daily Activity	Time
	6:00am		1:00pm
	7:00am		2:00pm
	8:00am		3:00pm
	9:00am		4:00pm
	10:00am		5:00pm
	11:00am		6:00pm
	12:00pm		7:00pm

Daily Prayer List *(Before you go to sleep tonight, who in your life requires prayer or what circumstance requires prayer today?)*

1. _____   2. _____

3. _____   4. _____

Prayer Focus: Psalm 112:5   Date: _____

A good man deals graciously and lends; He will guide his affairs with discretion.

How does this verse speak to your soul, heart, and mind?

_____

_____

_____

Daily Gratitude Prayer *(Consider a prayer like the following each morning before you start your day: Lord, thank you for this day. Lord, I am grateful for my health. Lord, thank you for trusting me to serve your people.)*

_____

_____

_____

Spend Time with God *(How did you spend time with God today? Did you pray, read scripture, or share His word with someone?)*

Daily Activity	Time	Daily Activity	Time
	6:00am		1:00pm
	7:00am		2:00pm
	8:00am		3:00pm
	9:00am		4:00pm
	10:00am		5:00pm
	11:00am		6:00pm
	12:00pm		7:00pm

Daily Prayer List *(Before you go to sleep tonight, who in your life requires prayer or what circumstance requires prayer today?)*

1. _____   2. _____

3. _____   4. _____

Prayer Focus: Psalm 37:23   Date: _____

The steps of a good man are ordered by the LORD, And He delights in his way.

How does this verse speak to your soul, heart, and mind?

_____

_____

_____

Daily Gratitude Prayer *(Consider a prayer like the following each morning before you start your day: Lord, thank you for this day. Lord, I am grateful for my health. Lord, thank you for trusting me to serve your people.)*

_____

_____

_____

Spend Time with God *(How did you spend time with God today? Did you pray, read scripture, or share His word with someone?)*

Daily Activity	Time	Daily Activity	Time
	6:00am		1:00pm
	7:00am		2:00pm
	8:00am		3:00pm
	9:00am		4:00pm
	10:00am		5:00pm
	11:00am		6:00pm
	12:00pm		7:00pm

Daily Prayer List (Before you go to sleep tonight, who in your life requires prayer or what circumstance requires prayer today?)

1. _____   2. _____

3. _____   4. _____

Prayer Focus: 2 Kings 6:16
Date: _____

So, he answered, Do not fear, for those who are with us are more than those who are with them.

How does this verse speak to your soul, heart, and mind?

_____

_____

_____

Daily Gratitude Prayer *(Consider a prayer like the following each morning before you start your day: Lord, thank you for this day. Lord, I am grateful for my health. Lord, thank you for trusting me to serve your people.)*

_____

_____

_____

Spend Time with God *(How did you spend time with God today? Did you pray, read scripture, or share His word with someone?)*

Daily Activity	Time	Daily Activity	Time
	6:00am		1:00pm
	7:00am		2:00pm
	8:00am		3:00pm
	9:00am		4:00pm
	10:00am		5:00pm
	11:00am		6:00pm
	12:00pm		7:00pm

Daily Prayer List *(Before you go to sleep tonight, who in your life requires prayer or what circumstance requires prayer today?)*

1. _____   2. _____

3. _____   4. _____

Prayer Focus: Galatians 6:9   Date: _____

And let us not grow weary while doing good, for in due season we shall reap if we do not lose heart.

How does this verse speak to your soul, heart, and mind?

_____

_____

_____

Daily Gratitude Prayer *(Consider a prayer like the following each morning before you start your day: Lord, thank you for this day. Lord, I am grateful for my health. Lord, thank you for trusting me to serve your people.)*

_____

_____

_____

Spend Time with God *(How did you spend time with God today? Did you pray, read scripture, or share His word with someone?)*

Daily Activity	Time	Daily Activity	Time
	6:00am		1:00pm
	7:00am		2:00pm
	8:00am		3:00pm
	9:00am		4:00pm
	10:00am		5:00pm
	11:00am		6:00pm
	12:00pm		7:00pm

Daily Prayer List *(Before you go to sleep tonight, who in your life requires prayer or what circumstance requires prayer today?)*

1. _____   2. _____

3. _____   4. _____

Prayer Focus: Luke 9:62   Date: _____

But Jesus said to him, "No one, having put his hand to the plow, and looking back, is fit for the kingdom of God."

How does this verse speak to your soul, heart, and mind?

_____

_____

_____

Daily Gratitude Prayer *(Consider a prayer like the following each morning before you start your day: Lord, thank you for this day. Lord, I am grateful for my health. Lord, thank you for trusting me to serve your people.)*

_____

_____

_____

Spend Time with God *(How did you spend time with God today? Did you pray, read scripture, or share His word with someone?)*

Daily Activity	Time	Daily Activity	Time
	6:00am		1:00pm
	7:00am		2:00pm
	8:00am		3:00pm
	9:00am		4:00pm
	10:00am		5:00pm
	11:00am		6:00pm
	12:00pm		7:00pm

Daily Prayer List *(Before you go to sleep tonight, who in your life requires prayer or what circumstance requires prayer today?)*

1. _____   2. _____

3. _____   4. _____

Prayer Focus: Matthew 5:7   **Date:** _____

Blessed are the merciful, for they shall obtain mercy.

How does this verse speak to your soul, heart, and mind?

_____

_____

_____

Daily Gratitude Prayer *(Consider a prayer like the following each morning before you start your day: Lord, thank you for this day. Lord, I am grateful for my health. Lord, thank you for trusting me to serve your people.)*

_____

_____

_____

Spend Time with God *(How did you spend time with God today? Did you pray, read scripture, or share His word with someone?)*

Daily Activity	Time	Daily Activity	Time
	6:00am		1:00pm
	7:00am		2:00pm
	8:00am		3:00pm
	9:00am		4:00pm
	10:00am		5:00pm
	11:00am		6:00pm
	12:00pm		7:00pm

Daily Prayer List (Before you go to sleep tonight, who in your life requires prayer or what circumstance requires prayer today?)

1. _____   2. _____

3. _____   4. _____

Prayer Focus: James 1:19   Date: _____

My dear brothers and sisters, take note of this: Everyone should be quick to listen, slow to speak and slow to become angry.

How does this verse speak to your soul, heart, and mind?

_____

_____

_____

Daily Gratitude Prayer *(Consider a prayer like the following each morning before you start your day: Lord, thank you for this day. Lord, I am grateful for my health. Lord, thank you for trusting me to serve your people.)*

_____

_____

_____

Spend Time with God *(How did you spend time with God today? Did you pray, read scripture, or share His word with someone?)*

Daily Activity	Time	Daily Activity	Time
	6:00am		1:00pm
	7:00am		2:00pm
	8:00am		3:00pm
	9:00am		4:00pm
	10:00am		5:00pm
	11:00am		6:00pm
	12:00pm		7:00pm

Daily Prayer List *(Before you go to sleep tonight, who in your life requires prayer or what circumstance requires prayer today?)*

1. _____   2. _____

3. _____   4. _____

Prayer Focus: Psalm 119:105   **Date:** _____

Your word is a lamp to my feet and a light to my path.

How does this verse speak to your soul, heart, and mind?

_____

_____

_____

Daily Gratitude Prayer *(Consider a prayer like the following each morning before you start your day: Lord, thank you for this day. Lord, I am grateful for my health. Lord, thank you for trusting me to serve your people.)*

_____

_____

_____

Spend Time with God *(How did you spend time with God today? Did you pray, read scripture, or share His word with someone?)*

Daily Activity	Time	Daily Activity	Time
	6:00am		1:00pm
	7:00am		2:00pm
	8:00am		3:00pm
	9:00am		4:00pm
	10:00am		5:00pm
	11:00am		6:00pm
	12:00pm		7:00pm

Daily Prayer List (Before you go to sleep tonight, who in your life requires prayer or what circumstance requires prayer today?)

1. _____   2. _____

3. _____   4. _____

Prayer Focus: Proverbs 7:1   Date: _____

My son, keep my words and treasure my commandments within you.

How does this verse speak to your soul, heart, and mind?

_____

_____

_____

Daily Gratitude Prayer *(Consider a prayer like the following each morning before you start your day: Lord, thank you for this day. Lord, I am grateful for my health. Lord, thank you for trusting me to serve your people.)*

_____

_____

_____

Spend Time with God *(How did you spend time with God today? Did you pray, read scripture, or share His word with someone?)*

Daily Activity	Time	Daily Activity	Time
	6:00am		1:00pm
	7:00am		2:00pm
	8:00am		3:00pm
	9:00am		4:00pm
	10:00am		5:00pm
	11:00am		6:00pm
	12:00pm		7:00pm

Daily Prayer List *(Before you go to sleep tonight, who in your life requires prayer or what circumstance requires prayer today?)*

1. _____   2. _____

3. _____   4. _____

Prayer Focus: Psalm 61:8   Date: _____

So, I will sing praise to Your name forever, That I may daily perform my vows.

How does this verse speak to your soul, heart, and mind?

_____

_____

_____

Daily Gratitude Prayer *(Consider a prayer like the following each morning before you start your day: Lord, thank you for this day. Lord, I am grateful for my health. Lord, thank you for trusting me to serve your people.)*

_____

_____

_____

Spend Time with God *(How did you spend time with God today? Did you pray, read scripture, or share His word with someone?)*

Daily Activity	Time	Daily Activity	Time
	6:00am		1:00pm
	7:00am		2:00pm
	8:00am		3:00pm
	9:00am		4:00pm
	10:00am		5:00pm
	11:00am		6:00pm
	12:00pm		7:00pm

Daily Prayer List (Before you go to sleep tonight, who in your life requires prayer or what circumstance requires prayer today?)

1. _____   2. _____

3. _____   4. _____

Prayer Focus: Romans 8:25   Date: _____

But if we hope for what we do not see, we eagerly wait for it with perseverance.

How does this verse speak to your soul, heart, and mind?

_____

_____

_____

Daily Gratitude Prayer *(Consider a prayer like the following each morning before you start your day: Lord, thank you for this day. Lord, I am grateful for my health. Lord, thank you for trusting me to serve your people.)*

_____

_____

_____

Spend Time with God *(How did you spend time with God today? Did you pray, read scripture, or share His word with someone?)*

Daily Activity	Time	Daily Activity	Time
	6:00am		1:00pm
	7:00am		2:00pm
	8:00am		3:00pm
	9:00am		4:00pm
	10:00am		5:00pm
	11:00am		6:00pm
	12:00pm		7:00pm

Daily Prayer List (Before you go to sleep tonight, who in your life requires prayer or what circumstance requires prayer today?)

1. _____   2. _____

3. _____   4. _____

Prayer Focus: Proverbs 3:7-8   Date: _____

Do not be wise in your own eyes; Fear the LORD and depart from evil. It will be health to your flesh, And strength to your bones.

How does this verse speak to your soul, heart, and mind?

_____

_____

_____

Daily Gratitude Prayer *(Consider a prayer like the following each morning before you start your day: Lord, thank you for this day. Lord, I am grateful for my health. Lord, thank you for trusting me to serve your people.)*

_____

_____

_____

Spend Time with God *(How did you spend time with God today? Did you pray, read scripture, or share His word with someone?)*

Daily Activity	Time	Daily Activity	Time
	6:00am		1:00pm
	7:00am		2:00pm
	8:00am		3:00pm
	9:00am		4:00pm
	10:00am		5:00pm
	11:00am		6:00pm
	12:00pm		7:00pm

Daily Prayer List *(Before you go to sleep tonight, who in your life requires prayer or what circumstance requires prayer today?)*

1. _____   2. _____

3. _____   4. _____

Prayer Focus: Jeremiah 30:17a
Date: _____

For I will restore health to you and heal you of your wounds.

How does this verse speak to your soul, heart, and mind?

_____

_____

_____

Daily Gratitude Prayer *(Consider a prayer like the following each morning before you start your day: Lord, thank you for this day. Lord, I am grateful for my health. Lord, thank you for trusting me to serve your people.)*

_____

_____

_____

Spend Time with God *(How did you spend time with God today? Did you pray, read scripture, or share His word with someone?)*

Daily Activity	Time	Daily Activity	Time
	6:00am		1:00pm
	7:00am		2:00pm
	8:00am		3:00pm
	9:00am		4:00pm
	10:00am		5:00pm
	11:00am		6:00pm
	12:00pm		7:00pm

Daily Prayer List (Before you go to sleep tonight, who in your life requires prayer or what circumstance requires prayer today?)

1. _____   2. _____

3. _____   4. _____

Prayer Focus: 1 Peter 5:6   Date: _____

Humble yourselves therefore under the mighty hand of God, that he may exalt you in due time.

How does this verse speak to your soul, heart, and mind?

_____

_____

_____

Daily Gratitude Prayer *(Consider a prayer like the following each morning before you start your day: Lord, thank you for this day. Lord, I am grateful for my health. Lord, thank you for trusting me to serve your people.)*

_____

_____

_____

Spend Time with God *(How did you spend time with God today? Did you pray, read scripture, or share His word with someone?)*

Daily Activity	Time	Daily Activity	Time
	6:00am		1:00pm
	7:00am		2:00pm
	8:00am		3:00pm
	9:00am		4:00pm
	10:00am		5:00pm
	11:00am		6:00pm
	12:00pm		7:00pm

Daily Prayer List (Before you go to sleep tonight, who in your life requires prayer or what circumstance requires prayer today?)

1. _____   2. _____

3. _____   4. _____

Prayer Focus: Ecclesiastes 2:26   Date: _____

For God gives wisdom and knowledge and joy to a man who is good in His sight.

How does this verse speak to your soul, heart, and mind?

_____

_____

_____

Daily Gratitude Prayer *(Consider a prayer like the following each morning before you start your day: Lord, thank you for this day. Lord, I am grateful for my health. Lord, thank you for trusting me to serve your people.)*

_____

_____

_____

Spend Time with God *(How did you spend time with God today? Did you pray, read scripture, or share His word with someone?)*

Daily Activity	Time	Daily Activity	Time
	6:00am		1:00pm
	7:00am		2:00pm
	8:00am		3:00pm
	9:00am		4:00pm
	10:00am		5:00pm
	11:00am		6:00pm
	12:00pm		7:00pm

Daily Prayer List (Before you go to sleep tonight, who in your life requires prayer or what circumstance requires prayer today?)

1. _____   2. _____

3. _____   4. _____

Prayer Focus: Psalm 1:1   Date: _____

Blessed is the man Who walks not in the counsel of the ungodly, nor stands in the path of sinners, Nor sits in the seat of the scornful.

How does this verse speak to your soul, heart, and mind?

_____

_____

_____

Daily Gratitude Prayer *(Consider a prayer like the following each morning before you start your day: Lord, thank you for this day. Lord, I am grateful for my health. Lord, thank you for trusting me to serve your people.)*

_____

_____

_____

Spend Time with God *(How did you spend time with God today? Did you pray, read scripture, or share His word with someone?)*

Daily Activity	Time	Daily Activity	Time
	6:00am		1:00pm
	7:00am		2:00pm
	8:00am		3:00pm
	9:00am		4:00pm
	10:00am		5:00pm
	11:00am		6:00pm
	12:00pm		7:00pm

Daily Prayer List *(Before you go to sleep tonight, who in your life requires prayer or what circumstance requires prayer today?)*

1. _____

2. _____

3. _____

4. _____

Prayer Focus: Psalm 37:23   Date: _____

The LORD makes firm the steps of the one who delights in him.

How does this verse speak to your soul, heart, and mind?

_____

_____

_____

Daily Gratitude Prayer *(Consider a prayer like the following each morning before you start your day: Lord, thank you for this day. Lord, I am grateful for my health. Lord, thank you for trusting me to serve your people.)*

_____

_____

_____

Spend Time with God *(How did you spend time with God today? Did you pray, read scripture, or share His word with someone?)*

Daily Activity	Time	Daily Activity	Time
	6:00am		1:00pm
	7:00am		2:00pm
	8:00am		3:00pm
	9:00am		4:00pm
	10:00am		5:00pm
	11:00am		6:00pm
	12:00pm		7:00pm

Daily Prayer List *(Before you go to sleep tonight, who in your life requires prayer or what circumstance requires prayer today?)*

1. _____   2. _____

3. _____   4. _____

Prayer Focus: Romans 12:17   Date: _____

Do not repay anyone evil for evil. Be careful to do what is right in the eyes of everyone.

How does this verse speak to your soul, heart, and mind?

_____

_____

_____

Daily Gratitude Prayer *(Consider a prayer like the following each morning before you start your day: Lord, thank you for this day. Lord, I am grateful for my health. Lord, thank you for trusting me to serve your people.)*

_____

_____

_____

Spend Time with God *(How did you spend time with God today? Did you pray, read scripture, or share His word with someone?)*

Daily Activity	Time	Daily Activity	Time
	6:00am		1:00pm
	7:00am		2:00pm
	8:00am		3:00pm
	9:00am		4:00pm
	10:00am		5:00pm
	11:00am		6:00pm
	12:00pm		7:00pm

Daily Prayer List *(Before you go to sleep tonight, who in your life requires prayer or what circumstance requires prayer today?)*

1. _____   2. _____

3. _____   4. _____

Prayer Focus: Song of Solomon 8:7   Date: _____

Many waters cannot quench love; rivers cannot sweep it away. If one were to give all the wealth of one's house for love, it would be utterly scorned.

How does this verse speak to your soul, heart, and mind?

_____

_____

_____

Daily Gratitude Prayer *(Consider a prayer like the following each morning before you start your day: Lord, thank you for this day. Lord, I am grateful for my health. Lord, thank you for trusting me to serve your people.)*

_____

_____

_____

Spend Time with God *(How did you spend time with God today? Did you pray, read scripture, or share His word with someone?)*

Daily Activity	Time	Daily Activity	Time
	6:00am		1:00pm
	7:00am		2:00pm
	8:00am		3:00pm
	9:00am		4:00pm
	10:00am		5:00pm
	11:00am		6:00pm
	12:00pm		7:00pm

Daily Prayer List *(Before you go to sleep tonight, who in your life requires prayer or what circumstance requires prayer today?)*

1. _____   2. _____

3. _____   4. _____

Prayer Focus: Hebrews 10:30   Date: _____

Therefore, putting away lying, "Let each one of you speak truth with his neighbor," for we are members of one another.

How does this verse speak to your soul, heart, and mind?

_____

_____

_____

Daily Gratitude Prayer *(Consider a prayer like the following each morning before you start your day: Lord, thank you for this day. Lord, I am grateful for my health. Lord, thank you for trusting me to serve your people.)*

_____

_____

_____

Spend Time with God *(How did you spend time with God today? Did you pray, read scripture, or share His word with someone?)*

Daily Activity	Time	Daily Activity	Time
	6:00am		1:00pm
	7:00am		2:00pm
	8:00am		3:00pm
	9:00am		4:00pm
	10:00am		5:00pm
	11:00am		6:00pm
	12:00pm		7:00pm

Daily Prayer List *(Before you go to sleep tonight, who in your life requires prayer or what circumstance requires prayer today?)*

1. _____   2. _____

3. _____   4. _____

Prayer Focus: 2 Timothy 2:15   Date: _____

Do your best to present yourself to God as one approved, a worker who does not need to be ashamed and who correctly handles the word of truth.

How does this verse speak to your soul, heart, and mind?

_____

_____

_____

Daily Gratitude Prayer *(Consider a prayer like the following each morning before you start your day: Lord, thank you for this day. Lord, I am grateful for my health. Lord, thank you for trusting me to serve your people.)*

_____

_____

_____

Spend Time with God *(How did you spend time with God today? Did you pray, read scripture, or share His word with someone?)*

Daily Activity	Time	Daily Activity	Time
	6:00am		1:00pm
	7:00am		2:00pm
	8:00am		3:00pm
	9:00am		4:00pm
	10:00am		5:00pm
	11:00am		6:00pm
	12:00pm		7:00pm

Daily Prayer List (Before you go to sleep tonight, who in your life requires prayer or what circumstance requires prayer today?)

1. _____   2. _____

3. _____   4. _____

Prayer Focus: Exodus 14:14   Date: _____

The LORD will fight for you, and you shall hold your peace.

How does this verse speak to your soul, heart, and mind?

_____

_____

_____

Daily Gratitude Prayer *(Consider a prayer like the following each morning before you start your day: Lord, thank you for this day. Lord, I am grateful for my health. Lord, thank you for trusting me to serve your people.)*

_____

_____

_____

Spend Time with God *(How did you spend time with God today? Did you pray, read scripture, or share His word with someone?)*

Daily Activity	Time	Daily Activity	Time
	6:00am		1:00pm
	7:00am		2:00pm
	8:00am		3:00pm
	9:00am		4:00pm
	10:00am		5:00pm
	11:00am		6:00pm
	12:00pm		7:00pm

Daily Prayer List (Before you go to sleep tonight, who in your life requires prayer or what circumstance requires prayer today?)

1. _____   2. _____

3. _____   4. _____

Prayer Focus: 1 Peter 3:13   Date: _____

Who is going to harm you if you are eager to do good?

How does this verse speak to your soul, heart, and mind?

_____

_____

_____

Daily Gratitude Prayer *(Consider a prayer like the following each morning before you start your day: Lord, thank you for this day. Lord, I am grateful for my health. Lord, thank you for trusting me to serve your people.)*

_____

_____

_____

Spend Time with God *(How did you spend time with God today? Did you pray, read scripture, or share His word with someone?)*

Daily Activity	Time	Daily Activity	Time
	6:00am		1:00pm
	7:00am		2:00pm
	8:00am		3:00pm
	9:00am		4:00pm
	10:00am		5:00pm
	11:00am		6:00pm
	12:00pm		7:00pm

Daily Prayer List *(Before you go to sleep tonight, who in your life requires prayer or what circumstance requires prayer today?)*

1. _____   2. _____

3. _____   4. _____

Prayer Focus: Romans 12:21   Date: _____

Do not be overcome by evil but overcome evil with good.

How does this verse speak to your soul, heart, and mind?

_____

_____

_____

Daily Gratitude Prayer *(Consider a prayer like the following each morning before you start your day: Lord, thank you for this day. Lord, I am grateful for my health. Lord, thank you for trusting me to serve your people.)*

_____

_____

_____

Spend Time with God *(How did you spend time with God today? Did you pray, read scripture, or share His word with someone?)*

Daily Activity	Time	Daily Activity	Time
	6:00am		1:00pm
	7:00am		2:00pm
	8:00am		3:00pm
	9:00am		4:00pm
	10:00am		5:00pm
	11:00am		6:00pm
	12:00pm		7:00pm

Daily Prayer List *(Before you go to sleep tonight, who in your life requires prayer or what circumstance requires prayer today?)*

1. _____   2. _____

3. _____   4. _____

Prayer Focus: Psalm 147:3   Date: _____

He heals the brokenhearted and binds up their wounds.

How does this verse speak to your soul, heart, and mind?

_____

_____

_____

Daily Gratitude Prayer *(Consider a prayer like the following each morning before you start your day: Lord, thank you for this day. Lord, I am grateful for my health. Lord, thank you for trusting me to serve your people.)*

_____

_____

_____

Spend Time with God *(How did you spend time with God today? Did you pray, read scripture, or share His word with someone?)*

Daily Activity	Time	Daily Activity	Time
	6:00am		1:00pm
	7:00am		2:00pm
	8:00am		3:00pm
	9:00am		4:00pm
	10:00am		5:00pm
	11:00am		6:00pm
	12:00pm		7:00pm

Daily Prayer List (Before you go to sleep tonight, who in your life requires prayer or what circumstance requires prayer today?)

1. _____   2. _____

3. _____   4. _____

Prayer Focus: Revelation 21:4   Date: _____

He will wipe every tear from their eyes. There will be no more death' or mourning or crying or pain, for the old order of things has passed away.

How does this verse speak to your soul, heart, and mind?

_____

_____

_____

Daily Gratitude Prayer *(Consider a prayer like the following each morning before you start your day: Lord, thank you for this day. Lord, I am grateful for my health. Lord, thank you for trusting me to serve your people.)*

_____

_____

_____

Spend Time with God *(How did you spend time with God today? Did you pray, read scripture, or share His word with someone?)*

Daily Activity	Time	Daily Activity	Time
	6:00am		1:00pm
	7:00am		2:00pm
	8:00am		3:00pm
	9:00am		4:00pm
	10:00am		5:00pm
	11:00am		6:00pm
	12:00pm		7:00pm

Daily Prayer List (Before you go to sleep tonight, who in your life requires prayer or what circumstance requires prayer today?)

1. _____

2. _____

3. _____

4. _____

Prayer Focus: Psalm 4:8   Date: _____

In peace I will lie down and sleep, for you alone, LORD, make me dwell in safety.

How does this verse speak to your soul, heart, and mind?

_____

_____

_____

Daily Gratitude Prayer *(Consider a prayer like the following each morning before you start your day: Lord, thank you for this day. Lord, I am grateful for my health. Lord, thank you for trusting me to serve your people.)*

_____

_____

_____

Spend Time with God *(How did you spend time with God today? Did you pray, read scripture, or share His word with someone?)*

Daily Activity	Time	Daily Activity	Time
	6:00am		1:00pm
	7:00am		2:00pm
	8:00am		3:00pm
	9:00am		4:00pm
	10:00am		5:00pm
	11:00am		6:00pm
	12:00pm		7:00pm

Daily Prayer List (Before you go to sleep tonight, who in your life requires prayer or what circumstance requires prayer today?)

1. _____   2. _____

3. _____   4. _____

Prayer Focus: James 3:18

Date: _____

Now the fruit of righteousness is sown in peace by those who make peace.

How does this verse speak to your soul, heart, and mind?

_____

_____

_____

Daily Gratitude Prayer *(Consider a prayer like the following each morning before you start your day: Lord, thank you for this day. Lord, I am grateful for my health. Lord, thank you for trusting me to serve your people.)*

_____

_____

_____

Spend Time with God *(How did you spend time with God today? Did you pray, read scripture, or share His word with someone?)*

Daily Activity	Time	Daily Activity	Time
	6:00am		1:00pm
	7:00am		2:00pm
	8:00am		3:00pm
	9:00am		4:00pm
	10:00am		5:00pm
	11:00am		6:00pm
	12:00pm		7:00pm

Daily Prayer List (Before you go to sleep tonight, who in your life requires prayer or what circumstance requires prayer today?)

1. _____

2. _____

3. _____

4. _____

Prayer Focus: Isaiah 32:8   Date: _____

But a generous man devises generous things, and by generosity he shall stand.

How does this verse speak to your soul, heart, and mind?

_____

_____

_____

Daily Gratitude Prayer *(Consider a prayer like the following each morning before you start your day: Lord, thank you for this day. Lord, I am grateful for my health. Lord, thank you for trusting me to serve your people.)*

_____

_____

_____

Spend Time with God *(How did you spend time with God today? Did you pray, read scripture, or share His word with someone?)*

Daily Activity	Time	Daily Activity	Time
	6:00am		1:00pm
	7:00am		2:00pm
	8:00am		3:00pm
	9:00am		4:00pm
	10:00am		5:00pm
	11:00am		6:00pm
	12:00pm		7:00pm

Daily Prayer List *(Before you go to sleep tonight, who in your life requires prayer or what circumstance requires prayer today?)*

1. _____   2. _____

3. _____   4. _____

Prayer Focus: Matthew 26:41   Date: _____

"Watch and pray so that you will not fall into temptation. The spirit is willing, but the flesh is weak."

How does this verse speak to your soul, heart, and mind?

_____

_____

_____

Daily Gratitude Prayer *(Consider a prayer like the following each morning before you start your day: Lord, thank you for this day. Lord, I am grateful for my health. Lord, thank you for trusting me to serve your people.)*

_____

_____

_____

Spend Time with God *(How did you spend time with God today? Did you pray, read scripture, or share His word with someone?)*

Daily Activity	Time	Daily Activity	Time
	6:00am		1:00pm
	7:00am		2:00pm
	8:00am		3:00pm
	9:00am		4:00pm
	10:00am		5:00pm
	11:00am		6:00pm
	12:00pm		7:00pm

Daily Prayer List (Before you go to sleep tonight, who in your life requires prayer or what circumstance requires prayer today?)

1. _____   2. _____

3. _____   4. _____

Prayer Focus: James 5:16   Date: _____

Confess your trespasses to one another, and pray for one another, that you may be healed. The effective, fervent prayer of a righteous man avails much.

How does this verse speak to your soul, heart, and mind?

_____

_____

_____

Daily Gratitude Prayer *(Consider a prayer like the following each morning before you start your day: Lord, thank you for this day. Lord, I am grateful for my health. Lord, thank you for trusting me to serve your people.)*

_____

_____

_____

Spend Time with God *(How did you spend time with God today? Did you pray, read scripture, or share His word with someone?)*

Daily Activity	Time	Daily Activity	Time
	6:00am		1:00pm
	7:00am		2:00pm
	8:00am		3:00pm
	9:00am		4:00pm
	10:00am		5:00pm
	11:00am		6:00pm
	12:00pm		7:00pm

Daily Prayer List (Before you go to sleep tonight, who in your life requires prayer or what circumstance requires prayer today?)

1. _____   2. _____

3. _____   4. _____

Prayer Focus: 1 Thessalonians 5:17   Date: _____

Pray without ceasing.

How does this verse speak to your soul, heart, and mind?

_____

_____

_____

Daily Gratitude Prayer *(Consider a prayer like the following each morning before you start your day: Lord, thank you for this day. Lord, I am grateful for my health. Lord, thank you for trusting me to serve your people.)*

_____

_____

_____

Spend Time with God *(How did you spend time with God today? Did you pray, read scripture, or share His word with someone?)*

Daily Activity	Time	Daily Activity	Time
	6:00am		1:00pm
	7:00am		2:00pm
	8:00am		3:00pm
	9:00am		4:00pm
	10:00am		5:00pm
	11:00am		6:00pm
	12:00pm		7:00pm

Daily Prayer List (Before you go to sleep tonight, who in your life requires prayer or what circumstance requires prayer today?)

1. _____   2. _____

3. _____   4. _____

Prayer Focus: 1 Chronicles 16:11   Date: _____

Seek the LORD and His strength; Seek His face evermore!

How does this verse speak to your soul, heart, and mind?

_____

_____

_____

Daily Gratitude Prayer *(Consider a prayer like the following each morning before you start your day: Lord, thank you for this day. Lord, I am grateful for my health. Lord, thank you for trusting me to serve your people.)*

_____

_____

_____

Spend Time with God *(How did you spend time with God today? Did you pray, read scripture, or share His word with someone?)*

Daily Activity	Time	Daily Activity	Time
	6:00am		1:00pm
	7:00am		2:00pm
	8:00am		3:00pm
	9:00am		4:00pm
	10:00am		5:00pm
	11:00am		6:00pm
	12:00pm		7:00pm

Daily Prayer List *(Before you go to sleep tonight, who in your life requires prayer or what circumstance requires prayer today?)*

1. _____   2. _____

3. _____   4. _____

Prayer Focus: 1 John 5:15   Date: _____

And if we know that he hears us—whatever we ask—we know that we have what we asked of him.

How does this verse speak to your soul, heart, and mind?

_____

_____

_____

Daily Gratitude Prayer *(Consider a prayer like the following each morning before you start your day: Lord, thank you for this day. Lord, I am grateful for my health. Lord, thank you for trusting me to serve your people.)*

_____

_____

_____

Spend Time with God *(How did you spend time with God today? Did you pray, read scripture, or share His word with someone?)*

Daily Activity	Time	Daily Activity	Time
	6:00am		1:00pm
	7:00am		2:00pm
	8:00am		3:00pm
	9:00am		4:00pm
	10:00am		5:00pm
	11:00am		6:00pm
	12:00pm		7:00pm

Daily Prayer List (Before you go to sleep tonight, who in your life requires prayer or what circumstance requires prayer today?)

1. _____ 2. _____

3. _____ 4. _____

Prayer Focus: Mark 4:8   Date: _____

Still other seed fell on good soil. It came up, grew and produced a crop, some multiplying thirty, some sixty, some a hundred times.

How does this verse speak to your soul, heart, and mind?

_____

_____

_____

Daily Gratitude Prayer *(Consider a prayer like the following each morning before you start your day: Lord, thank you for this day. Lord, I am grateful for my health. Lord, thank you for trusting me to serve your people.)*

_____

_____

_____

Spend Time with God *(How did you spend time with God today? Did you pray, read scripture, or share His word with someone?)*

Daily Activity	Time	Daily Activity	Time
	6:00am		1:00pm
	7:00am		2:00pm
	8:00am		3:00pm
	9:00am		4:00pm
	10:00am		5:00pm
	11:00am		6:00pm
	12:00pm		7:00pm

Daily Prayer List *(Before you go to sleep tonight, who in your life requires prayer or what circumstance requires prayer today?)*

1. _____   2. _____

3. _____   4. _____

Prayer Focus: Psalm 26:11   Date: _____

But as for me, I will walk in my integrity; Redeem me and be merciful to me.

How does this verse speak to your soul, heart, and mind?

_____

_____

_____

Daily Gratitude Prayer *(Consider a prayer like the following each morning before you start your day: Lord, thank you for this day. Lord, I am grateful for my health. Lord, thank you for trusting me to serve your people.)*

_____

_____

_____

Spend Time with God *(How did you spend time with God today? Did you pray, read scripture, or share His word with someone?)*

Daily Activity	Time	Daily Activity	Time
	6:00am		1:00pm
	7:00am		2:00pm
	8:00am		3:00pm
	9:00am		4:00pm
	10:00am		5:00pm
	11:00am		6:00pm
	12:00pm		7:00pm

Daily Prayer List *(Before you go to sleep tonight, who in your life requires prayer or what circumstance requires prayer today?)*

1. _____   2. _____

3. _____   4. _____

Prayer Focus: Matthew 11:28   Date: _____

Come to Me, all you who labor and are heavy laden, and I will give you rest.

How does this verse speak to your soul, heart, and mind?

_____

_____

_____

Daily Gratitude Prayer *(Consider a prayer like the following each morning before you start your day: Lord, thank you for this day. Lord, I am grateful for my health. Lord, thank you for trusting me to serve your people.)*

_____

_____

_____

Spend Time with God *(How did you spend time with God today? Did you pray, read scripture, or share His word with someone?)*

Daily Activity	Time	Daily Activity	Time
	6:00am		1:00pm
	7:00am		2:00pm
	8:00am		3:00pm
	9:00am		4:00pm
	10:00am		5:00pm
	11:00am		6:00pm
	12:00pm		7:00pm

Daily Prayer List (Before you go to sleep tonight, who in your life requires prayer or what circumstance requires prayer today?)

1. _____   2. _____

3. _____   4. _____

Prayer Focus: Isaiah 32:17   Date: _____

The work of righteousness will be peace, And the effect of righteousness, quietness and assurance forever.

How does this verse speak to your soul, heart, and mind?

_____

_____

_____

Daily Gratitude Prayer *(Consider a prayer like the following each morning before you start your day: Lord, thank you for this day. Lord, I am grateful for my health. Lord, thank you for trusting me to serve your people.)*

_____

_____

_____

Spend Time with God *(How did you spend time with God today? Did you pray, read scripture, or share His word with someone?)*

Daily Activity	Time	Daily Activity	Time
	6:00am		1:00pm
	7:00am		2:00pm
	8:00am		3:00pm
	9:00am		4:00pm
	10:00am		5:00pm
	11:00am		6:00pm
	12:00pm		7:00pm

Daily Prayer List *(Before you go to sleep tonight, who in your life requires prayer or what circumstance requires prayer today?)*

1. _____   2. _____

3. _____   4. _____

Prayer Focus: Romans 3:23   Date: _____

For all have sinned and fall short of the glory of God.

How does this verse speak to your soul, heart, and mind?

_____

_____

_____

Daily Gratitude Prayer *(Consider a prayer like the following each morning before you start your day: Lord, thank you for this day. Lord, I am grateful for my health. Lord, thank you for trusting me to serve your people.)*

_____

_____

_____

Spend Time with God *(How did you spend time with God today? Did you pray, read scripture, or share His word with someone?)*

Daily Activity	Time	Daily Activity	Time
	6:00am		1:00pm
	7:00am		2:00pm
	8:00am		3:00pm
	9:00am		4:00pm
	10:00am		5:00pm
	11:00am		6:00pm
	12:00pm		7:00pm

Daily Prayer List *(Before you go to sleep tonight, who in your life requires prayer or what circumstance requires prayer today?)*

1. _____   2. _____

3. _____   4. _____

Prayer Focus: Proverbs 3:26   Date: _____

For the LORD will be your confidence and will keep your foot from being caught.

How does this verse speak to your soul, heart, and mind?

_____

_____

_____

Daily Gratitude Prayer *(Consider a prayer like the following each morning before you start your day: Lord, thank you for this day. Lord, I am grateful for my health. Lord, thank you for trusting me to serve your people.)*

_____

_____

_____

Spend Time with God *(How did you spend time with God today? Did you pray, read scripture, or share His word with someone?)*

Daily Activity	Time	Daily Activity	Time
	6:00am		1:00pm
	7:00am		2:00pm
	8:00am		3:00pm
	9:00am		4:00pm
	10:00am		5:00pm
	11:00am		6:00pm
	12:00pm		7:00pm

Daily Prayer List *(Before you go to sleep tonight, who in your life requires prayer or what circumstance requires prayer today?)*

1. _____   2. _____

3. _____   4. _____

Prayer Focus: Philippians 1:6   Date: _____

Being confident of this very thing, that He who has begun a good work in you will complete it until the day of Jesus Christ.

How does this verse speak to your soul, heart, and mind?

_____

_____

_____

Daily Gratitude Prayer *(Consider a prayer like the following each morning before you start your day: Lord, thank you for this day. Lord, I am grateful for my health. Lord, thank you for trusting me to serve your people.)*

_____

_____

_____

Spend Time with God *(How did you spend time with God today? Did you pray, read scripture, or share His word with someone?)*

Daily Activity	Time	Daily Activity	Time
	6:00am		1:00pm
	7:00am		2:00pm
	8:00am		3:00pm
	9:00am		4:00pm
	10:00am		5:00pm
	11:00am		6:00pm
	12:00pm		7:00pm

Daily Prayer List *(Before you go to sleep tonight, who in your life requires prayer or what circumstance requires prayer today?)*

1. _____   2. _____

3. _____   4. _____

Prayer Focus: Proverbs 11:30   Date: _____

The fruit of the righteous is a tree of life, and the one who is wise saves lives.

How does this verse speak to your soul, heart, and mind?

_____

_____

_____

Daily Gratitude Prayer *(Consider a prayer like the following each morning before you start your day: Lord, thank you for this day. Lord, I am grateful for my health. Lord, thank you for trusting me to serve your people.)*

_____

_____

_____

Spend Time with God *(How did you spend time with God today? Did you pray, read scripture, or share His word with someone?)*

Daily Activity	Time	Daily Activity	Time
	6:00am		1:00pm
	7:00am		2:00pm
	8:00am		3:00pm
	9:00am		4:00pm
	10:00am		5:00pm
	11:00am		6:00pm
	12:00pm		7:00pm

Daily Prayer List *(Before you go to sleep tonight, who in your life requires prayer or what circumstance requires prayer today?)*

1. _____   2. _____

3. _____   4. _____

Prayer Focus: Psalm 73:26   Date: _____

My flesh and my heart fail; But God is the strength of my heart and my portion forever.

How does this verse speak to your soul, heart, and mind?

_____

_____

_____

Daily Gratitude Prayer *(Consider a prayer like the following each morning before you start your day: Lord, thank you for this day. Lord, I am grateful for my health. Lord, thank you for trusting me to serve your people.)*

_____

_____

_____

Spend Time with God *(How did you spend time with God today? Did you pray, read scripture, or share His word with someone?)*

Daily Activity	Time	Daily Activity	Time
	6:00am		1:00pm
	7:00am		2:00pm
	8:00am		3:00pm
	9:00am		4:00pm
	10:00am		5:00pm
	11:00am		6:00pm
	12:00pm		7:00pm

Daily Prayer List *(Before you go to sleep tonight, who in your life requires prayer or what circumstance requires prayer today?)*

1. _____
2. _____
3. _____
4. _____

Prayer Focus: Genesis 24:40a   Date: _____

The LORD, before whom I walk, will send His angel with you and prosper your way.

How does this verse speak to your soul, heart, and mind?

_____

_____

_____

Daily Gratitude Prayer *(Consider a prayer like the following each morning before you start your day: Lord, thank you for this day. Lord, I am grateful for my health. Lord, thank you for trusting me to serve your people.)*

_____

_____

_____

Spend Time with God *(How did you spend time with God today? Did you pray, read scripture, or share His word with someone?)*

Daily Activity	Time	Daily Activity	Time
	6:00am		1:00pm
	7:00am		2:00pm
	8:00am		3:00pm
	9:00am		4:00pm
	10:00am		5:00pm
	11:00am		6:00pm
	12:00pm		7:00pm

Daily Prayer List *(Before you go to sleep tonight, who in your life requires prayer or what circumstance requires prayer today?)*

1. _____   2. _____

3. _____   4. _____

Prayer Focus: Ephesians 6:8   Date: _____

knowing that whatever good anyone does, he will receive the same from the Lord, whether he is a slave or free.

How does this verse speak to your soul, heart, and mind?

_____

_____

_____

Daily Gratitude Prayer *(Consider a prayer like the following each morning before you start your day: Lord, thank you for this day. Lord, I am grateful for my health. Lord, thank you for trusting me to serve your people.)*

_____

_____

_____

Spend Time with God *(How did you spend time with God today? Did you pray, read scripture, or share His word with someone?)*

Daily Activity	Time	Daily Activity	Time
	6:00am		1:00pm
	7:00am		2:00pm
	8:00am		3:00pm
	9:00am		4:00pm
	10:00am		5:00pm
	11:00am		6:00pm
	12:00pm		7:00pm

Daily Prayer List *(Before you go to sleep tonight, who in your life requires prayer or what circumstance requires prayer today?)*

1. _____   2. _____

3. _____   4. _____

Prayer Focus: Psalms 92:4   Date: _____

For You, LORD, have made me glad through Your work; I will triumph in the works of Your hands.

How does this verse speak to your soul, heart, and mind?

_____

_____

_____

Daily Gratitude Prayer *(Consider a prayer like the following each morning before you start your day: Lord, thank you for this day. Lord, I am grateful for my health. Lord, thank you for trusting me to serve your people.)*

_____

_____

_____

Spend Time with God *(How did you spend time with God today? Did you pray, read scripture, or share His word with someone?)*

Daily Activity	Time	Daily Activity	Time
	6:00am		1:00pm
	7:00am		2:00pm
	8:00am		3:00pm
	9:00am		4:00pm
	10:00am		5:00pm
	11:00am		6:00pm
	12:00pm		7:00pm

Daily Prayer List *(Before you go to sleep tonight, who in your life requires prayer or what circumstance requires prayer today?)*

1. _____   2. _____

3. _____   4. _____

Prayer Focus: Deuteronomy 24:19b   Date: _____

The LORD your God may bless you in all the work of your hands.

How does this verse speak to your soul, heart, and mind?

_____

_____

_____

Daily Gratitude Prayer *(Consider a prayer like the following each morning before you start your day: Lord, thank you for this day. Lord, I am grateful for my health. Lord, thank you for trusting me to serve your people.)*

_____

_____

_____

Spend Time with God *(How did you spend time with God today? Did you pray, read scripture, or share His word with someone?)*

Daily Activity	Time	Daily Activity	Time
	6:00am		1:00pm
	7:00am		2:00pm
	8:00am		3:00pm
	9:00am		4:00pm
	10:00am		5:00pm
	11:00am		6:00pm
	12:00pm		7:00pm

Daily Prayer List (Before you go to sleep tonight, who in your life requires prayer or what circumstance requires prayer today?)

1. _____   2. _____

3. _____   4. _____

Made in United States
North Haven, CT
23 December 2021

13579462R00202